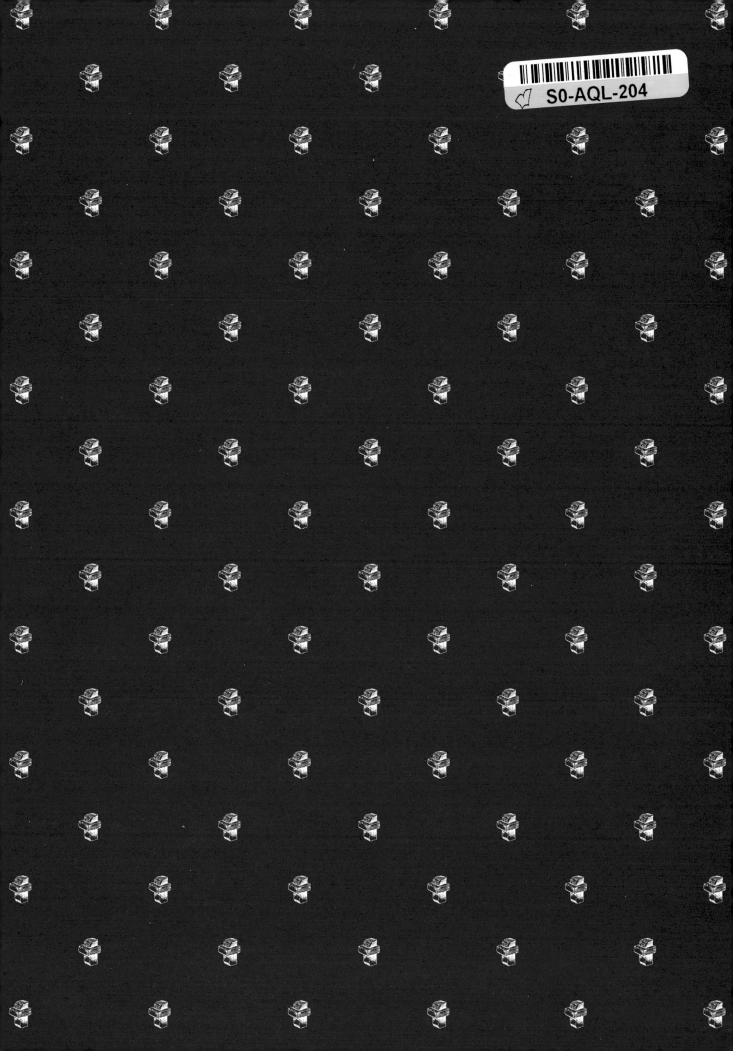

THE ARTS & CRAFTS PRICE GUIDE

FURNITURE

Gustav Stickley
L & JG Stickley
Charles Stickley
Roycroft

A DECADE OF AUCTION RESULTS
1987-1997

A PRESENTATION BY TREADWAY GALLERY, INC. OF CINCINNATI, OHIO
IN ASSOCIATION WITH THE JOHN TOOMEY GALLERY OF OAK PARK, ILLINOIS

First edition published in 1998 by Treadway Gallery Inc.
Under the direction of Don Treadway

Printed in the U.S.A. by Image Graphics Inc., Paducah Kentucky

ISBN 1-893148-02-5

Cover design: Teresa Dorsey/Treadway Gallery
Editorial and Illustration: Stephen Large/Treadway Gallery

First published in the United States in 1998 by
Treadway Gallery Inc.
2029 Madison Road
Cincinnati, Ohio 45208
Phone: (513) 321-6742
Fax: (513) 871-7722
E-mail: Treadway 2029@Earthlink.net
Web Site: www.treadwaygallery.com

INTRODUCTION

As we approach the 21st Century and the 100th Anniversary of the Arts & Crafts Movement in America, we have witnessed the emergence of Gustav Stickley and his contemporaries to a significant place in the world of collecting. The interest in the designs by makers from this period has rivaled that of any in the antique world. Comparatively, the Arts & Crafts market is a recent phenomenon with much scholarly research being done regarding both the social and artistic aspects, but collectors are also looking for sources to help determine the value of their pieces. Many people question why similar forms can vary greatly in price and, understandably, they are looking for answers.

The goal of this book is simply to help Arts & Crafts collectors and dealers identify different forms and track their selling price through a decade of our auctions from 1987 thru 1997. This should be one of several reference books that can be used to help understand this developing market. Price guides traditionally give one auction result or a retail asking price that are quickly obsolete. We have tried to present a more comprehensive look at this market with most forms having multiple listings. This is very important in analyzing these fluctuating prices. We have provided this data in an easy to follow format with the majority of these objects being photographed and separated into basic categories, identifying the maker, condition, date sold and actual selling price. In most cases, interpreting this information will provide a logical market trend. Certainly, variation in price often can be attributed to the condition and finish of the object, or the state of the market in the year in which it was sold. Sometimes, however, auction results can dramatically differ on the same piece for no apparent reason, therefore, establishing the actual current value of a piece is impossible through a price guide. Still, the first step in arriving at a fair value in any market is studying comparables.

Because we have been the premier auction house over the past ten years in terms of number of pieces sold and consistency of performance, this book should prove to be the most helpful guide available for evaluating pieces from the Arts & Crafts period.

At $20,900 this Roycroft china cabinet set an auction record besting two other Roycroft records we set at our February 1995 sale.

CONDITIONS OF SALE

The objects in this book were sold following these guidelines.

"**Furniture** retains the original hardware and wood unless otherwise noted. Finishes are carefully described as are markings. The wood is oak, unless otherwise stated, and the dimensions are approximate. The furniture is old and over the years has undoubtedly acquired a few dents, drink rings, separations, burns, chips and assorted flaws. We will only mention those that we feel are objectionable. When we describe a piece of furniture as being in "excellent condition", it generally implies that the finish is original, and the structure is in fine shape. A piece that has been totally or partially refinished and is in good structural shape will generally be described as being in "very good condition". A piece that needs to be refinished or that has a less than stable structural state (i.e. needs gluing, redoweling, etc.) may be generally described as being in "good condition". When we use the term "attribution", it means that we believe it to be made by the maker to whom we attribute it. We don't guarantee it to be so, it's purely our opinion. The majority of this furniture is ready to be put in the home."

One piece of a Gustav Stickley bedroom set
that sold for $49,500 establishing a world record
in September 1989.

We want to purchase objects outright or take on consignment for our future auctions. One piece or a collection are of interest. We can arrange delivery or personally pick up objects throughout the country.

We have an established international clientele base that we feel is the best in the business. That clientele has enabled us to establish more world record prices than any of our competitors.

Expertise - Our expertise in the field of the 20th Century objects is second to none. The prices we obtain can attest to that.

Commission - These terms are flexible for special consignments.

Payments - Payment is made in 30 business days or less.

Catalog - Our catalogs are exceptional. Please compare our 20th Century catalog with our competition to judge for yourself. This quality is a key to our success.

Advertising - We advertise worldwide and maintain the largest and most active mailing list in the industry.

Photography - Consignors will be pleased to note there is no charge for photography. Our catalogs contain high-quality, professional photos.

Estimates - We invite you to bring or send photographs of your property for our estimates. Evaluations of the property can be conducted in your home by contacting Don Treadway at 513-321-6742. In Chicago, contact John Toomey at 708-383-5234.

WE BUY OUTRIGHT OR AUCTION ON YOUR BEHALF. CALL US FOR OUR ESTIMATES.

This Gustav Stickley corner cabinet
sold for $26,400 at our November 1992 sale.

BOOKCASES

1. **Gustav Stickley** bookcase, #700, single door case designed by Harvey Ellis, three leaded sections at top, columns with capitals at sides, arched toe-board, original finish, paper label and red decal, 35"w x 14"d x 58"h, minor splitting to exterior back, excellent condition 10,000-15,000   May 21, 1995   Sold for $12,000

2. **Gustav Stickley** bookcase, #703, Harvey Ellis designed double door bookcase, mahogany, eight leaded panes atop each door, columns with capitals at center and sides, arched apron, original finish, red decal, 48"w x 14"d x 58"h, excellent condition   9000-11,000   November 17, 1991 Sold for $9000

To buy, consign or sell these objects call:
(513) 321-6742 or (708) 383-5234

3. **Gustav Stickley** bookcase, #703 1/2, open bookcase designed by Harvey Ellis, architectural columns with capitals at sides, arched toe board, adjustable shelves, red decal, Eastwood paper label, original finish, 60"w x 14"d x 58"h, excellent condition   5500-7500 December 3, 1995 Sold for $14,000

Not Pictured:

4. **Gustav Stickley** bookcase, #703 1/2, red decal, Eastwood label, original finish, excellent condition   5500-7500 December 3, 1995 Sold for $12,000 **Note: Same form as preceding one.**

5. **Gustav Stickley** bookcase, #715, single door with sixteen panes, double-keyed tenons at top and bottom, iron hardware, original finish, red decal, 39"w x 13"d x 56"h, excellent condition 2500-3500   November 14, 1993 Sold for $5000

Not Pictured:

6. **Gustav Stickley** bookcase, #715, recoated original finish, red decal, paper label, very good condition   3000-3500   September 30, 1990 Sold for $2900

7. **Gustav Stickley** bookcase, #715, light recoat over original finish, signed with black decal, very good condition   5500-6500 February 16, 1997   Sold for $5500

8. **Gustav Stickley** bookcase, #715, single door with sixteen panes and original iron hardware, recent finish, unsigned, 35"w x 13"d x 56"h, very good condition   3000-3500   February 13, 1994 Sold for $3750   **Note: Same form as preceding #715 without keyed tenons.**

Not Pictured:

9. **Gustav Stickley** bookcase, #715, recent finish, unsigned, very good condition   2000-3000 October 2, 1988   Sold for $1750

10. **Gustav Stickley** bookcase, #715, paper label, original finish, some scratches, very good condition 2500-3500   March 25, 1990   Sold for $3750

11. **Gustav Stickley** bookcase, #715, paper label, recent finish, some staining top, very good condition 2500-3000   April 7, 1991   Sold for $3000

12. **Gustav Stickley** bookcase, #715, original finish, red decal, excellent condition   2000-3000 November 15, 1992   Sold for $3750

13. **Gustav Stickley** bookcase, #715, original finish, red decal, minor stains to top, very good condition 3500-4500   May 21, 1995   Sold for $3500

14. **Gustav Stickley** bookcase, #715, original finish, red decal, minor rings on top, very good condition 3500-4500   August 27, 1995   Sold for $4250

15. **Gustav Stickley** bookcase, #715, original finish, red decal and paper label, excellent condition 4500-5500   August 25, 1996   Sold for $5500

16. **Gustav Stickley** bookcase, designed by Harvey Ellis, double glass doors over double wooden cabinet, arched apron, copper hardware, original light finish interior, original finish exterior, red decal, 42"w x 14"d x 64"h, excellent condition   15,000-20,000 May 3, 1992   Sold for $19,000

Not Pictured:

17. **Gustav Stickley** bookcase, original finish, signed large red decal, crack to one pane, veneer chips to one door, some distress to edges, very good condition 9000-12,000 November 24, 1996   Sold for $15,000 **Note: Same form as preceding one.**

18. **Gustav Stickley** bookcase, #542, double doors with mitered mullions and iron hardware, fixed shelves and thru-tenons with paneled back, 56"h x 36"w x 12"d, unmarked, recent finish, very good condition   2500-3000   March 25, 1990
Sold for $4250

Not Pictured:

19. **Gustav Stickley** bookcase, narrow two door form with eight panes per door and original iron V-pulls, original finish, branded signature, 35"w x 13"d x 56"h, minor restoration, very good condition   3500-4500   November 23, 1997   Sold for $4250

20. **Gustav Stickley** bookcase, #716, double doors, each with eight panes of glass, thru-tenon construction, original V-pulls, original finish, red decal, paper label, 48"w x 56"h, excellent condition   4000-5000   August 27, 1995
Sold for $4750

Not Pictured:

21. **Gustav Stickley** bookcase, #716, cleaned original finish, branded, very good condition   3000-4500
September 30, 1990   Sold for $3250

22. **Gustav Stickley** bookcase, #717, two doors each with eight panes and original copper hardware, slab sides with thru-tenon construction, recent finish, red decal, 48"w x 13"d x 56"h, very good condition   3500-4500
May 4, 1997   Sold for $4500

23. **Gustav Stickley** bookcase, #717, original finish, signed with black decal and Eastwood paper label, some roughness to lower tenons, very good condition   5000-6000
August 24, 1997   Sold for $5500

24. **Gustav Stickley** bookcase, #718, keyed-tenon construction, two doors with twelve panes per door, original iron hardware, original finish, Eastwood paper label and decal, 57"w x 13"d x 57"h, excellent condition 6000-8000   November 24, 1996 Sold for $7500

25. **Gustav Stickley** bookcase, #525, double door bookcase with keyed tenons top and bottom, mitered mullions, 42"w x 12"d x 56"h, recent finish, very good condition   3000-4000   November 17, 1991 Sold for $2600

26. **Gustav Stickley** bookcase, #523, two-door with six panes per door, original iron pulls, keyed tenons on sides, original finish, minor stains to top, branded signature, 41"w x 12"d x 44"h, excellent condition   3500-4500
May 21, 1995 Sold for $6000

27. **Gustav Stickley** bookcase, #719, has two doors with twelve panes per door and original iron pulls, original finish, branded, 60"w x 13"d x 57"h, excellent condition   5000-7000
May 21, 1995   Sold for $7500

Not Pictured:

28. **Gustav Stickley** bookcase, #719, original finish, paper label and red decal, very good condition
4000-5000   November 15, 1992
Sold for $4250

29. **Gustav Stickley** bookcase, #719, original finish, branded, minor repairs, very good condition
4500-5500   February 12, 1995
Sold for $7000

30. **Gustav Stickley** bookcase, #719, original copper hardware, original finish, red decal, minor stains to top, excellent condition   6500-8500
May 4, 1997   Sold for $7000

31. **Gustav Stickley** bookcase, #718, original finish, red decal, 54"w, very good condition   4500-5500 August 25, 1996 Sold for $5000 **Note: More narrow version of #719.**

32. **Gustav Stickley** bookcase, #718, original finish, red decal and paper label, very good condition 5500-7500   May 19, 1996 Sold for $5000

33. Gustav Stickley bookcase, two doors with diamond pattern to mullions, interior is open, 41"w x 64"h x 24"d, paper label, branded mark, original finish, excellent condition   7000-9000   March 27, 1988 Sold for $4500

34. Gustav Stickley three-door book-case, twelve panes of glass to each door with mitered mullions and early copper hardware, original finish, light interior, red decal, 73"w x 12"d x 56"h, excellent condition 15,000-20,000 May 21, 1995 Sold for $17,000

15

35. **Gustav Stickley** open bookcase, chamfered back and heavy thru-tenon construction on sides, recent finish, red decal, 31"w x 12"d x 56"h, very good condition   1200-1500 November 14, 1993   Sold for $2700

36. **L & JG Stickley** bookcase, #652, single door, peaked gallery, arched apron, thru-tenons, original finish, marked "The Work of...", 22"w x 11"d x 51"h, excellent condition   2500-3500   February 14, 1993 Sold for $3500

Not Pictured:

37. **L & JG Stickley** bookcase, #652, recent finish, signed metal tag, very good condition   3000-4000 February 16, 1997   Sold for $3250

38. **L & JG Stickley** bookcase, #641, single door case with twelve panes from Onondaga Shops, original hardware, keyed tenons to sides, original finish, unsigned, 34"w x 12"d x 57"h, excellent condition 4000-5000 February 12, 1995 Sold for $6000

39. **L & JG Stickley** bookcase, #641, single door with sixteen panes of glass and original, early copper pull, keyed tenon construction, chamfered back, original finish, unsigned, 40"w x 12"d x 58"h, excellent condition 5500-6500 March 3, 1996 Sold for $6000

Not Pictured:

40. **L & JG Stickley** bookcase, #641, chamfered board back, original finish, signed with a Handcraft decal, excellent condition 4000-5000 February 16, 1997 Sold for $6500

41. **L & JG Stickley** bookcase, #641, chamfered board back, original finish, signed with a Handcraft decal, excellent condition 4000-5000 February 16, 1997 Sold for $5500

42. **L & JG Stickley** bookcase, single door with sixteen panes, original copper hardware, keyed construction at top and bottom, original finish, Handcraft decal, 39"w x 12"d x 55"h, excellent condition   5000-6000   December 3, 1995 Sold for $5000

Not Pictured:

43. **L & JG Stickley** bookcase, single door with sixteen panes, keyed-tenon construction, original finish, branded, excellent condition 3000-4000   October 23, 1994   Sold for $5500 **Note: Same form as preceding one.**

44. **L & JG Stickley** bookcase, #638, double door case with arched base, recoated original finish, some stains to top, 48"w x 14"d x 48"h, very good condition   2000-3000 November 17, 1991   Sold for $2700

Not Pictured:

45. **L & JG Stickley** bookcase, #638, original finish, conjoined label, excellent condition   3000-4000 October 23, 1994   Sold for $3750

46. **L & JG Stickley** bookcase, #643, eight panes of glass on double doors, keyed tenons at sides, original finish, signed "The Work of....", one pull has been replaced, 40"w x 12"d x 55"h, very good condition   3000-4000   May 15, 1994 Sold for $3750

Not Pictured:

47. **L & JG Stickley** bookcase, #643, original finish, Handcraft decal, excellent condition   2500-3500 March 24, 1991   Sold for $4000

48. **L & JG Stickley** bookcase, #643, cleaned original finish, signed "The Work of...", very good condition 4500-5500   August 24, 1997   Sold for $4500

49. **L & JG Stickley** bookcase, #645, double door with twelve panes each, original copper hardware, keyed tenon construction, original finish, branded signature, 48"w x 12"d x 56"h, excellent condition 5500-6500   March 3, 1996 Sold for $6500

Not Pictured:

50. **L & JG Stickley** bookcase, #645, original finish, one cracked pane of glass, "Work of..." decal, excellent condition 3500-4500   April 7, 1991 Sold for $4250

51. **L & JG Stickley** bookcase, #645, original finish, unsigned, very good condition 5500-6500   May 19, 1996 Sold for $4500

To buy, consign or sell these objects call: (513) 321-6742 or (708) 383-5234

52. **L & JG Stickley** bookcase, Onondaga Shops, two door with twelve panes to each, keyed-tenon construction with chamfered back, original finish, unsigned, very good condition   5500-6500 February 12, 1995 Sold for $7000

53. **L & JG Stickley** three-door bookcase, #647, twelve panes to each door, original hammered copper hardware, original finish, numbered, 73"w x 12"d x 58"h, excellent condition   9000-12,000 December 3, 1995   Sold for $10,000

54. L & JG Stickley
bookcase, #331, Onondaga Shops three door case, keyed-tenons, twelve panes to each door, early hammered copper hardware, original finish, minor restoration, numbered, 74"w x 12"d x 57"h, very good condition
9000-12,000
October 23, 1994
Sold for $20,000

55. L & JG Stickley open bookcase, #642, thru-tenons top & bottom, two handcraft decals, recent finish, 30"w x 12"d x 55"h, very good condition
1200-1500   March 27, 1988   Sold for $1200

21

56. **L & JG Stickley** open bookcase, #646, chamfered back with keyed-tenons, recent finish, unsigned, 49"w x 12"d x 55"h, very good condition   1200-1500
October 23, 1994   Sold for $2200

Not Pictured:

57. **Charles Stickley** open bookcase, attribution, slab sides with keyed tenon construction, chamfered back, recent finish, unsigned, 41.5"w x 11"d x 56"h, very good condition   2000-3000   August 25, 1996
Sold for $3000   **Note: Quite similar to one pictured.**

58. **Charles Stickley** bookcase, single door with sixteen panes and original brass hardware, slab sides with thru-tenon construction and chamfered board back, original finish, unsigned, 37"w x 13"d x 56"h, excellent condition 3500-4500   May 4, 1997   Sold for $3500

59. Roycroft thirty-third degree bookcase, #086, single door with sixteen panes, one pane replaced, original hardware, original finish, marked with incised orb, 40"w x 15"d x 55"h, excellent condition   5000-6000   May 15, 1994 Sold for $4750

60. Roycroft thirty-third degree bookcase, #086, leaded glass door, original brass hardware, lightly cleaned original finish, orb mark, 46"w x 14"d x 55"h, minor repair to one side, very good condition   3500-4500 February 13, 1994   Sold for $7500

Not Pictured:

61. Roycroft thirty-third degree bookcase, #086, mahogany, replaced pull with original backplate, original finish with some color enhancement, orb mark, very good condition 3000-4000   November 15, 1992 Sold for $4000

62. Roycroft thirty-third degree bookcase, #086, mahogany, leaded glass, engraved name at top of door, cleaned original finish, orb mark, very good condition   3500-4500 February 12, 1995   Sold for $4250

63. **Roycroft** bookcase, unusual narrow form with five open shelves over single drawer, hammered copper pulls, recent finish, orb signature, 34"w x 9"d x 66"h, very good condition   5000-7000   March 3, 1996 Sold for $7000

64. **Roycroft** bookcase, similar to #085, mahogany, triple door, original hammered copper and brass pulls, keyed tenon sides, three original shelves per section, orb signature, original finish, minor chips to top edge, 68"w x 16"d x 53"h, very good condition 7000-9000   December 3, 1995 Sold for $5000

65. **Roycroft** bookcase, #085, triple door, keyed tenons on sides, iron hinges and round pulls with back plates, overhanging top, arched backsplash, original finish, script signature across front, 66"w x 16"d x 62"h, excellent condition   7000-9000
November 17, 1991   Sold for $12,000

66. **Roycroft** bookcase, similar to #085, triple door, except the Roycroft mark is across a gently arched backsplash, keyed tenons on sides, black metal hinges and round pulls on doors with backplate, 69"wide with overhang, 62"h, 14"d, adjustable shelving, original finish, excellent condition 7000-9000   September 30, 1990   Sold for $13,000

Arts & Crafts Furniture
Reference Book

67. **Gustav Stickley** corner cabinet, #972, double doors with twenty-four panes, full iron strap hardware on lower cabinets, original finish, red decal, 45"w x 25"d x 70"h, excellent condition   15,000-20,000   November 15, 1992 Sold for $24,000

To buy, consign or sell these objects call:
(513) 321-6742 or (708) 383-5234

68. **Gustav Stickley** china cabinet, single door with mitered mullions and original copper pull, chamfered board back, lightly cleaned original finish, signed with early red decal, 36"w x 14"d x 67"h, very good condition   10,000-15,000   May 4, 1997 Sold for $24,000

69. **Gustav Stickley** china cabinet, single door with sixteen glass panes and four panes to each side, original hammered copper hardware, original finish, branded signature, 36"w x 13"d x 59"h, excellent condition   4500-6500   May 19, 1996 Sold for $5500

Not Pictured:

70. **Gustav Stickley** china cabinet, original finish, branded signature, excellent condition   4500-6500 December 3, 1995   Sold for $6000 **Note: Same form as one pictured.**

71. **Gustav Stickley** china cabinet, #815, double doors, each with eight panes of glass, thru-tenon construction, original brass V- pulls, original finish, minor stains to top, branded signature, 40"w x 15"d x 64"h, very good condition   5000-6000   May 15, 1994   Sold for $7000

Not Pictured:

72. **Gustav Stickley** china cabinet, #815, original paper label, branded signature, excellent condition 5000-6000   October 2, 1988   Sold for $5750

73. **Gustav Stickley** china cabinet, #815, branded signature and paper label, separation to top, very good condition 6000-7000   December 3, 1995   Sold for $6000

74. **Gustav Stickley** china cabinet, #815, original finish, branded and paper label, excellent condition 7000-9000   May 21, 1995   Sold for $6000

75. **Gustav Stickley** china cabinet, #815, branded, original finish, small chip to one mullion, very good condition 5000-6000   February 12, 1995   Sold for $6000

76. **Gustav Stickley** china cabinet, #815, iron v-pulls on doors, three adjustable shelves, arched apron, original finish, red decal, 40"w x 15"d x 64"h, excellent condition   4500-6500
September 30, 1990   Sold for $5500 **Note: Same form as above except the wood is oak.**

Not Pictured:

77. **Gustav Stickley** china cabinet, #815, original mirrored upper back, arched apron, two replaced shelves, original finish, red decal, very good condition   4000-5000   March 24, 1991   Sold for $3250

78. **Gustav Stickley** china cabinet, #815, original iron hardware, original finish, red decal and remnant of paper label, excellent condition   7000-9000 February 16, 1997   Sold for $9500

79. **Gustav Stickley** china cabinet, #815, original finish, branded signature and paper label, excellent condition   6000-8000   November 23, 1997 Sold for $9000

80. **Gustav Stickley** china cabinet, #815, in mahogany, original brass hardware, original finish, red decal, excellent condition   6500-8500   May 19, 1996 Sold for $7000

To buy, consign or sell these objects call:
(513) 321-6742 or (708) 383-5234

81. **Gustav Stickley** china cabinet, similar to #815, double doors with twenty-four panes, arched apron, iron V-pulls, original finish, red decal, 52"w x 15"d x 64"h, excellent condition   6000-8000   May 2, 1993
Sold for $10,000   **Note: Same basic design as #815 with one additional row of panes in each door.**

82. **Gustav Stickley** china cabinet, #803, Harvey Ellis design with single arched door over an arched toe-board with bowed sides and chamfered back, original iron hardware, Eastwood paper label, recent finish, sanding marks to surface, 36"w x 15"d x 60"h, good condition   3500-4500
August 25, 1996 Sold for $4000

Not Pictured:

83. **Gustav Stickley** china cabinet, #803, replaced chamfered back, original finish, very good condition   3500-4500   November 14, 1993   Sold for $5500

84. **Gustav Stickley** china cabinet, #803, original finish, paper label, excellent condition   7000-9000
May 19, 1996 Sold for $8000

85. **Gustav Stickley** china cabinet, #820, single door with twelve panes, four panes to each side, original finish, signed with red decal, 36"w x 60"h, excellent condition   3500-4500   March 3, 1996 Sold for $4500

Not Pictured:

86. **Gustav Stickley** china cabinet, #820, recent finish, red decal and paper label, one corner side pane has chip, very good condition   2500-3500 May 15, 1994   Sold for $4250

87. **Gustav Stickley** china cabinet, #820, original copper hardware, original finish, red decal, 36"w x 15"d x 63"h, excellent condition   4500-5500 May 4, 1997   Sold for $5000

88. **Gustav Stickley** china cabinet, double doors with eight panes to each, glass sides, original V-pulls, original finish, branded signature, 42"w x 16"d x 63"h, excellent condition   5000-7000 October 23, 1994   Sold for $8500 **Note: Same design as #820 with two doors.**

89. **Gustav Stickley** china cabinet, two doors with eight panes each, four panes to each side, original finish, red decal, 36"w x 14"d x 56"h, excellent condition 4500-5500 May 21, 1995 Sold for $4750 **Note: Same form as preceding one with escutcheons rather than hardware and a bit more narrow.**

90. **L & JG Stickley** china cabinet, #761, single door with original copper hardware, overhanging top, arch to top of door and sides, three shelves, original finish, Handcraft decal, 36"w x 16"d x 60"h, excellent condition 3000-4000 May 21, 1995 Sold for $5500 **Note: Quite similar to Gustav #803 except the sides have arches like front.**

91. **L & JG Stickley** china cabinet, #727, single door with nine panes over an arched toe-board, original finish, signed "The Work of ...", 34"w x 15"d x 55"h, excellent condition   3500-4500   December 3, 1995 Sold for $4250

Not Pictured:

92. **L & JG Stickley** china closet, #727, original finish, excellent condition   3000-4000   April 7, 1991 Sold for $3700

93. **L & JG Stickley** china cabinet, #727, original finish, branded signature, excellent condition   4500-5500 March 3, 1996   Sold for $4500

94. **L & JG Stickley** china cabinet, #727, recent finish, branded signature, very good condition   3000-4000 May 19, 1996 Sold for $3750

95. **L & JG Stickley** china cabinet, #728, double door with eighteen panes, stationary shelves, arches top and bottom, original finish, 48"w x 15"d x 55"h, excellent condition   3000-4000 May 3, 1992   Sold for $3750

96. **L & JG Stickley** china cabinet, #746, two door with twelve leaded panes at top of each door above clear pane of glass, glass sides with top section having nine leaded panes, original copper pulls, signed "The Work of...", original finish, 44"w x 16"d x 62"h, excellent condition 6000-8000   February 12, 1995   Sold for $6500

Not Pictured:

97. **L & JG Stickley** china cabinet, #746, signed "The Work of...", original finish, excellent condition   4000-5000   April 7, 1991 Sold for $8000

98. **L & JG Stickley** china cabinet, #746, two doors and glass sides, top of each door has a twelve pane leaded glass section, top of each side has a nine pane leaded glass section, one fixed and two adjustable shelves, corbeled legs, original finish, Handcraft decal, 44"w x 16"d x 69"h, excellent condition   5000-7000   November 14, 1993 Sold for $6000   **Note: Same design as preceding one except this has corbels on legs and a bit taller.**

99. **L & JG Stickley** china cabinet, #746, two doors and glass sides, top of each door has a six pane section, top of each side has a four pane section, one fixed and two adjustable shelves, arched bottom, original finish, marked "The Work of...", 44"w x 16"d x 62"h, excellent condition   3500-4500   February 13, 1994   Sold for $5500   **Note: Same form as preceding one except fewer number of panes in top are divided by wood mullions.**

Not Pictured:

100. **L & JG Stickley** china cabinet #746, original finish, signed "The Work of...", 40"w x 15"d x 62"h, excellent condition   6500-7500   May 4, 1997   Sold for $6500

101. **Roycroft** china cabinet, similar to #07, cabinet with two door leaded glass front and leaded glass sides in a geometric design, original hammered copper pulls, recent finish, orb mark on hardware and case, 46"w x 21"d x 55"h, very good condition   4000-6000   October 23, 1994   Sold for $9000

102. Roycroft china cabinet, #05, two leaded glass doors and sides with central organic design dividing geometric pattern at top and bottom, original copper hardware and hinges, Mackmurdo feet, original finish, script signature, two side panels of glass replaced, 51"w x 23"d x 60"h, excellent condition   7500-9500   February 12, 1995
Sold for $19,000

103. Gustav Stickley sideboard, #1301, eight leg form heavily pegged with an unusual combination of square wooden knobs on four drawers, copper straps and oval pulls on side cabinet doors, signed with a large red decal, original finish, 70"w x 25"d x 50"h, very good condition   6000-8000   May 15, 1994   Sold for $8000

104. Gustav Stickley sideboard, #817, eight-legs with hammered iron hardware, original finish on base, cleaned top, Eastwood label, 70"w x 26"d x 50"h, excellent condition   5000-7500   March 24, 1991   Sold for $6500

105. Gustav Stickley sideboard, #814 1/2, three graduated drawers above single drawer, strap hinges on doors, original finish, burned mark, 56"w x 49"h x 22"d, excellent condition 4000-6000 September 30, 1990 Sold for $5750

Not Pictured:

106. Gustav Stickley sideboard, #814 1/2, original finish, branded and paper label, some roughness, very good condition 4000-5000 November 24, 1996 Sold for $4250

107. Gustav Stickley sideboard, #814 1/2, original finish, minor veneer repair, red decal and paper label, very good condition 3500-4500 December 3, 1995 Sold for $4000

108. Gustav Stickley sideboard, #814 1/2, original finish, excellent condition 3000-4000 November 17, 1991 Sold for $2900

109. Gustav Stickley sideboard, #814 1/2, original finish, one lock missing, branded, very good condition 4500-5500 February 16, 1997   Sold for $6000

110. Gustav Stickley sideboard, #816, one long drawer over three smaller drawers, flanked by side cabinets, original finish, branded signature, 48"w x 19"d x 46"h, minor stains and repair, very good condition 2500-3500 December 3, 1995 Sold for $2100 **Note: Similar form as #814 1/2 without the straps on doors and more narrow.**

111. Gustav Stickley sideboard, #814, thru-tenon construction, two cabinet doors with strap hinges flanking three half drawers over one long drawer, original V-pulls and plate rail, original finish, red decal, 66"w x 24"d x 49"h, excellent condition 5500-7500 May 19, 1996 Sold for $10,000

Not Pictured:

112. Gustav Stickley sideboard, #814, original finish, red decal, paper label, excellent condition 3500-4500 April 7, 1991 Sold for $4750

113. Gustav Stickley sideboard, #814, veneer damage to doors, original finish, red decal, good condition 2500-3000 May 15, 1994   Sold for $2900

114. Gustav Stickley sideboard, #814, recent finish, one lock broken, one replaced slat on plate rail, retailer's mark, very good condition 2500-3500 February 13, 1994   Sold for $3250

115. Gustav Stickley sideboard, #814, recoated original finish, branded, minor veneer loss, very good condition 3000-4000   May 3, 1992 Sold for $2600

116. Gustav Stickley sideboard, #814, original finish, chip to lower front leg, branded signature, 66"w x 24"d x 49"h, excellent condition 6500-7500 May 4, 1997 Sold for $7000

117. Gustav Stickley buffet, #955, two drawers and a straight apron above an open shelf over one long drawer with wooden faceted pulls, chamfered sides and heavy thru-tenon construction, original plate rail, original finish, red decal, 60"w x 24"d x 44"h, minor restoration to feet and some surface scratches to top, very good condition   9000-12,000 May 4, 1997 Sold for $15,000

118. Gustav Stickley server, #970, early server with double-keyed tenons, early iron hardware, notched lower shelf, original finish, rear dust cover replaced, minor repair to one tenon, 44"w x 20"d x 37"h, excellent condition 7500-9500   May 2, 1993 Sold for $7000

Not Pictured:

119. Gustav Stickley server, unsigned, original finish, 42"w x 21"d x 33"h, excellent condition 5000-7500 September 30, 1990 Sold for $9000 **Note: Same form as preceding one without backsplash and slightly different details.**

120. Gustav Stickley server, #802, overhanging top, two drawers, copper V-pulls, original finish, branded, 42"w x 18"d x 39"h, excellent condition   1750-2250 February 14, 1993 Sold for $2300

Not Pictured:

121. Gustav Stickley server, #802, original finish, branded signature, excellent condition 2500-3500   December 3, 1995 Sold for $2700

122. Gustav Stickley server, #802, two drawers with hammered copper hardware above arched apron, original finish, bowed and tapered legs, extended slab sides, signed in drawer, 42"w x 18"d x 40"h, excellent condition   2500-3500 November 15, 1992 Sold for $3000 **Note: Same form as preceding piece, but with arched skirt, tapered legs and longer sides.**

Not Pictured:

123. Gustav Stickley server, #802, recent finish, copper hardware, red decal, some veneer lifting on side, very good condition   1750-2000 November 14, 1993 Sold for $1900

124. Gustav Stickley server, #818, three drawers with original oval iron pulls and ooze leather, lower stretcher and slightly tapered legs, original finish, red decal, minor rings to top, 48"w x 20"d x 39"h, very good condition   3500-4500
March 3, 1996
Sold for $3250

Not Pictured:

125. Gustav Stickley server, #818, original finish, burned mark, excellent condition 3000-4000   May 7, 1989
Sold for $3850

126. Gustav Stickley server, #818, recent finish, red decal, very good condition 3000-4000   May 21, 1995
Sold for $3000

127. Gustav Stickley sideboard, #819, three drawers over one, oval pulls, original finish, red decal, 39"h x 48"l, excellent condition 2500-3500
October 2, 1988
Sold for $3250

Not Pictured:

128. Gustav Stickley server, #819, cleaned original finish, paper label, red decal, some roughness and veneer repair, good condition 2000-2500
February 16, 1997
Sold for $2900

41

129. Gustav Stickley server, two drawers over one long drawer, plate rail on back, original finish, red decal, veneer chips to side, some stains to top, 48"w x 20"d x 44"h, very good condition 1500-2000   May 21, 1995 Sold for $1600

130. L & JG Stickley sideboard, #745, four narrow drawers flanked by two cabinets with strap hinges all over one long drawer above an arched toe-board, original copper hardware and plate rail to back, Handcraft decal, original finish, 54"w x 24"d x 48"h, excellent condition 4500-5500   August 25, 1996 Sold for $6500

Not Pictured:

131. L & JG Stickley sideboard, #745, marked "The Work of...", original finish, some staining to top, very good condition   2000-2500 March 25, 1990 Sold for $4250

132. L & JG Stickley sideboard, #745, plate rail missing, recent finish, Handcraft decal, very good condition 1500-2000   March 3, 1996 Sold for $2200

133. L & JG Stickley sideboard, four center drawers divided by two paneled doors with copper strap hinges all over one long drawer, arched front, original hardware, original finish, signed "The Work of..." 54"w x 24"d x 42"h, minor stains to top, excellent condition
3500-4500   May 21, 1995
Sold for $3250

134. L & JG Stickley sideboard, #731, side cabinets flank four drawers over long linen drawer, hammered copper hardware, full strap on cabinets, recent finish, 72"w x 26"d x 50"h, very good condition
2500-3500
May 3, 1992
Sold for $3000

135. L & JG Stickley
sideboard, #709, paneled plate rail with curved shelf supported by two corbels above two cabinet doors with three short drawers on sides over one long drawer, original finish, signed "The Work of...", 54"w x 22"d x 48"h, excellent condition
2500-3500
August 27, 1995
Sold for $3500

136. L & JG Stickley sideboard, #734, three drawers with two cabinets on side over one long drawer, plate rail, original finish, Handcraft decal, 48"w x 20"d x 44"h, very good condition   2000-3000
May 19, 1996 Sold for $2800

Not Pictured:

137. L & JG Stickley sideboard #734, cleaned original finish, unsigned, some stains to top, very good condition
1500-2000   October 23, 1994
Sold for $2200

138. L & JG Stickley
sideboard, #738, two drawers divided by two cabinet drawers with copper strap hinges, three lined silver drawers to the interior of one cabinet, original finish, branded "The Work of...", 60"w x 21"d x 46"h, excellent condition   4500-5500
March 3, 1996
Sold for $4500

Not Pictured:

139. L & JG Stickley
sideboard, #738, one cabinet pull replaced, light over coat on original finish, branded, minor roughness to top, very good condition
2500-3500
November 23, 1997
Sold for $3000

140. L & JG Stickley server, #740, two drawers with original copper hardware over one narrow shelf above lower shelf, original plate rail to back, recent finish, Handcraft signature, 48"w x 11"d x 50"h, some restoration and veneer loss, overall roughness, good condition   1000-1500
December 3, 1995
Sold for $1000

141. L & JG Stickley server, #741, signed "The Work of...", 40"h x 44"w x 18"d, top refinished, excellent original finish on base
2500-3000 April 7, 1991
Sold for $2450

Not Pictured:

142. L & JG Stickley server, #741, original finish, remnant of decal, excellent condition 2000-3000
May 21, 1995 Sold for $3000

143. L & JG Stickley server, #741, cleaned copper pulls, original finish, unsigned, 44"w x 18"d x 39"h, excellent condition
1500-2000 August 27, 1995
Sold for $2500 **Note: Same form as preceding one with different hardware.**

144. L &JG Stickley server, #752, original medium red/brown finish, slight arch to skirt under top, 39" x 40", excellent condition   1000-1250   October 4, 1987 Sold for $1400

Not Pictured:

145. L &JG Stickley server, #752, original finish, Handcraft decal, excellent condition 1500-2500   September 30, 1990 Sold for $2300

146. L & JG Stickley server, #752, refinished top, original finish to base, Handcraft decal, very good condition   1500-2000 November 15, 1992   Sold for $1500

147. Charles Stickley sideboard, attribution, paneled plate rail with corbel-supported shelf, over cabinet with three center drawers flanked by two cabinets over one long drawer, original hammered brass hardware, recent finish, unsigned, 56"w x 22"d x 53"h, very good condition   2500-3500 March 3, 1996   Sold for $3500

Not Pictured:

148. Charles Stickley sideboard, attribution, some stains on top, original finish, excellent condition 2000-3000   April 7, 1991 Sold for $2600 **Note: Same form as preceding one.**

149. Charles Stickley sideboard, attribution, cabinets with brass strap hinges flank two small drawers over three over two drawers, oval pulls, arched apron and sides, panelled gallery, lock broken, recent finish, 70"w x 25"d x 51"h, very good condition 1500-2000   February 14, 1993 Sold for $2600

47

Arts & Crafts Furniture
Reference Book

150. Gustav Stickley chairs, set of seven, six sides, #356, one arm #356A, original leather back and seat and original tacks, original finish, paper label and red decal, sides 18"w x 17"d x 38"h, arm 26"w x 19"d x 38"h, excellent condition   20,000-25,000 November 23, 1997   Sold for $42,000

151. Gustav Stickley directors table, #631, large rectangular top supported by splayed legs on a shoe-foot base with detail of three raised wooden pegs on each leg, refinished top, original finish to base, red decal, 86"l x 47"w x 29"h, some restoration, very good condition   20,000-30,000 November 23, 1997   Sold for $14,000

152. Gustav Stickley table, hexagonal leather top over arched cross-stretcher with nipple, thru-tenon construction, red decal, original leather, original finish, 48"dia. x 30"h, excellent condition 9000-12,000   February 12, 1995 Sold for $24,000

49

153. Gustav Stickley side chairs, #1297, set of eight, three horizontal slats under arched top rail, original drop-in rush seat over a notched seat rail, original finish, red box mark, small chip to one chair, one chair has minor break to rush, 18"w x 17"d x 37"h, excellent condition   7000-9000   August 24, 1997 Sold for $9500

154. Gustav Stickley dining table, circular top over notched cross-stretchers and nipple at center, includes two original 12" leaves, original finish, branded signature, 48"dia. x 32"h, some veneer repair at apron, very good condition   2500-3500 August 24, 1997   Sold for $2400

155. Gustav Stickley table, #624, hexagonal top over six legs with notched cross-stretchers and nipple, recent finish, one board replaced, branded, 48"dia. x 30"h, good condition 3000-4000   August 27, 1995 Sold for $3750

156. Gustav Stickley spindle dining chairs, one arm #376, five sides #374, high back with nine spindles to back and seven under seat, original drop-in seats recovered in green leather, original finish, five with red decal, one is branded, arm 28"w x 23"d x 49"h, excellent condition   25,000-35,000
August 24, 1997   Sold for $40,000

157. Gustav Stickley dining table, #634, circular top over a trumpeted cross-stretcher with thru-tenon construction, five original leaves, original finish, red decal and paper label, 53.5"dia. x 28"h, excellent condition   10,000-15,000   August 24, 1997
Sold for $13,000

158. Gustav Stickley dining table, #634, center leg, thru-tenons, arched cross-stretchers, two leaves, original finish, remnant of paper label and branded, 54"d x 30"h, excellent condition   4000-6000
November 17, 1991
Sold for $6000

Not Pictured:

159. Gustav Stickley dining table, #634, six leaves, refinished top, cleaned base, branded, Craftsman paper label, very good condition   4000-5000
May 2, 1993 Sold for $7500

160. Gustav Stickley dining table, #634, original finish with some stains and separation to top, paper label and decal, leaves are missing, very good condition 4000-5000   November 14, 1993   Sold for $3750

161. Gustav Stickley dining table, #634, original finish, five leaves, red decal and paper label, excellent condition   5000-7000   May 15, 1994
Sold for $11,000

162. Gustav Stickley dining table, #634, refinished top, original finish to base, branded signature, 60"dia. x 29"h, three original leaves, very good condition 6000-8000   May 4, 1997   Sold for $7000

163. Gustav Stickley dining table, #634, six skirted original leaves, original finish, red decal, 54"dia. x 29"h, seven 11" leaves, excellent condition   7500-10,000
November 24, 1996   Sold for $15,000

164. Gustav Stickley dining table, #656, round top over flared pedestal base, four original 11" leaves, original finish, some veneer missing on feet, minor stains to top, red decal and paper label, 54"dia. x 29"h, very good condition 3000-4000 December 3, 1995 Sold for $6500

Not Pictured:

165. Gustav Stickley dining table, #656, recent finish, four leaves, 48"dia. x 30"h, very good condition 2500-3500 September 30, 1990 Sold for $2550

166. Gustav Stickley dining table, #656, five leaves, minor roughness to base, original finish, red decal and paper label, very good condition 3000-4000 April 7, 1991 Sold for $2700

167. Gustav Stickley dining table, #656, six leaves, original medium finish, paper label, excellent condition 3500-4500 May 3, 1992 Sold for $3500

168. Gustav Stickley dining table, #656, four leaves, original finish, minor chips to feet, signed with decal, excellent condition 3500-4500 November 14, 1993 Sold for $5000

169. Gustav Stickley dining table, four leaves, corbeled base, original finish on base, top refinished, repairs to apron, branded, 54"dia., very good condition 1500-2000 February 14, 1993 Sold for $2200 **Note: This and the following table are light forms produced after the #656.**

170. Gustav Stickley dining table, round table, four leaves, center pedestal with corbel supports on four feet, original finish, branded signature, 48"dia., loss of veneer, excellent condition 3500-4500 December 3, 1995 Sold for $2000

171. Gustav Stickley dining table, #632, circular top over five tapered legs, six leaves, original finish to base, some color added to top, signed red decal, 48"dia. x 30"h, excellent condition 4500-5500 May 19, 1996 Sold for $5000

Not Pictured:

172. Gustav Stickley dining table, #632, includes two original leaves, original finish, signed with red decal and paper label, 48"dia. x 29"h, minor veneer repair to apron, very good condition 3500-4500 November 23, 1997 Sold for $3750

173. Gustav Stickley dining table, #633, large and desirable form with circular top over five tapered legs, seven original leaves, some veneer repair and color added to original finish, signed red decal, 60"dia. x 28.5"h, very good condition 5500-7500 February 16, 1997 Sold for $6000 **Note: A larger example of #632.**

174. Gustav Stickley dining table, #418, fixed top table, wide overhang above octagonal apron, supports four tapered legs with cut-out corbels, recent finish, unsigned, 59"dia. x 30"h, very good condition   5000-7000   May 2, 1993   Sold for $7500

175. Gustav Stickley table, #407, leather top over splayed legs with an arched and keyed cross-stretcher base, replaced leather and recent finish, some wear to bottom of feet, 48"dia. x 30"h, very good condition 2000-3000   May 15, 1994 Sold for $2800

176. Gustav Stickley table, #633, circular top over four splayed legs with arched lower stretcher having keyed tenons and nippled center, original finish, signed with red decal, 44"dia. x 29"h , excellent condition   4500-5500 August 25, 1996   Sold for $6500

Not Pictured:

177. Gustav Stickley table, #633, original finish, signed with red decal, excellent condition   4500-5500   May 19, 1996 Sold for $4500

178. Gustav Stickley table, #636, thick circular top, tapered and splayed legs supported by arched and keyed cross-stretchers, original finish, red decal, 48"dia. x 30"h, excellent condition 6000-8000   December 3, 1995 Sold for $8500   **Note: Same basic form as #633, just a bit heavier and larger top.**

179. Gustav Stickley table, #636, original finish, red decal, excellent condition 5500-7500   May 19, 1996 Sold for $6500

180. Gustav Stickley table, early form with overhanging top, nippled cross-stretchers, original black finish on base, refinished top, 1902 decal, 40"dia. x 30"h, very good condition   3000-3500 December 3, 1995   Sold for $4250

181. Gustav Stickley table, #626, thru-tenons and arched stretchers, 40"dia. x 30"h, recent finish, red decal, very good condition
2000-3000   May 7, 1989
Sold for $2600

Not Pictured:

182. Gustav Stickley table, #626, top refinished, base original, paper label and red decal, very good condition   2000-2500
February 13, 1994   Sold for $1500

183. Gustav Stickley table, #627, round table with original finish, arched stretchers with facetted nipple in middle, red decal, 48"dia. x 30"h, excellent condition
2500-3500
March 24, 1991
Sold for $3550

Not Pictured:

184. Gustav Stickley table, #627, original finish, red decal, excellent condition   2000-3000
November 17, 1991
Sold for $2300

185. Gustav Stickley table, #627, original finish to base, top refinished, paper label, decal, very good condition   2000-2500
October 23, 1994
Sold for $2300

186. Gustav Stickley table, #627, original finish, red decal, veneer loss to legs, good condition
1000-1500   August 25, 1996
Sold for $1600

187. Gustav Stickley table, #439, trumpeted thru-tenon stretchers, original finish, signed with red box mark, 26"dia. x 26"h, excellent condition   2000-2500
May 15, 1994   Sold for $4500

188. Gustav Stickley table, #440, thick top and thru-tenons on top and bottom stretchers, thru post to top, crossed stretchers with nipple, recent finish, red decal, 30"dia. x 28"h, very good condition   1500-2000
May 2, 1993   Sold for $3000

189. Gustav Stickley table, #441, thru-tenons, stacked stretchers, nippled, cleaned original finish, red decal, 36"dia. x 30"h, very good condition   1500-2000
May 2, 1993   Sold for $2400

190. Gustav Stickley table, thru-post at top, stacked stretcher with facetted nipple, large red decal, recent finish, 40"dia. x 30"h, very good condition 1500-2000   November 24, 1996
Sold for $2000

191. Gustav Stickley table, #644, round top over notched cross-stretchers with nipple, some color added to original finish, remnant of paper label, 30"dia. x 29"h, very good condition 1500-2000 August 27, 1995 Sold for $2600

Not Pictured:

192. Gustav Stickley table, #643, recent finish, some restoration to legs, signed, paper label, 36"dia. x 29"h, good condition 1000-1500 August 25, 1996 Sold for $1300 **Note: A smaller version of #644.**

193. Gustav Stickley table, #644, recent finish, branded mark, very good condition 1500-2000 October 2, 1988 Sold for $2400

194. Gustav Stickley table, #644, paper label, cleaned original finish, some dark circles on top, veneer splitting on apron, very good condition 1250-1750 March 25, 1990 Sold for $1500

195. Gustav Stickley table, #644, recent finish, paper label under top, very good condition 800-1100 September 30, 1990 Sold for $1000

196. Gustav Stickley table, #645, original finish, red decal, paper label, 36"dia., slight veneer loss on apron, very good condition 1500-2000 November 17, 1991 Sold for $2000 **Note: A larger version of #644.**

197. Gustav Stickley table, #645, mahogany, recent finish, unsigned, some roughness, very good condition 1500-2000 March 3, 1996 Sold for $850

198. Gustav Stickley table, #646, recent finish, unsigned, 40"dia., minor restoration, very good condition 1000-1500 December 3, 1995 Sold for $1700 **Note: A larger version of #645.**

199. Gustav Stickley table, #646, early red mark, recent finish, excellent condition 2500-3000 May 7, 1989 Sold for $1500

200. Gustav Stickley table, #646, recent finish, remnant of paper label, very good condition 1200-1500 August 25, 1996 Sold for $1400

201. Gustav Stickley table, round top with protruding legs at edge, notched stretcher, thru-tenons, nippled, original finish, paper label, red decal, 30"dia. x 29"h, veneer chip on apron, excellent condition 1500-2000 February 14, 1993 Sold for $1900

202. Gustav Stickley table #609, center table with arched stretchers supporting lower round shelf, original finish, red decal, 36"dia. x 30"h, excellent condition 1500-2000   March 24, 1991 Sold for $1600

203. Gustav Stickley table, #609, original leather top and lower shelf, original finish, paper label, 36"w x 30"h, some stains and burns to top, very good condition   2500-3500 February 13, 1994   Sold for $4250

Not Pictured:

204. Gustav Stickley table, #609, brown leatherette cover replaced, recent finish, unsigned, very good condition 1000-1500   August 27, 1995 Sold for $1500

205. Gustav Stickley dining table, square top with cut corners over a cross-stretcher base with thru-tenon construction, two leaves, recent finish, unsigned, 54"square x 29"h, very good condition   6000-8000
August 25, 1996   Sold for $6500

206. L & JG Stickley dining table, #717, large round top over a slightly tapered center pedestal with four extending feet at base, three original 12" leaves, original finish, signed "The Work of...", 60"dia. x 30"h, excellent condition   6500-7500
August 25, 1996   Sold for $6000

Not Pictured:

207. L & JG Stickley dining table, #717, three 12" leaves, original finish, excellent condition
2500-3500   November 15, 1992   Sold for $2400

208. L & JG Stickley dining table, #716, five legs over a cruciform base, four 12"w leaves, original finish, minor stains to top, 42"dia. x 30"h, signed "The Work of...", excellent condition   3500-4500
May 21, 1995   Sold for $6000

Not Pictured:

209. L & JG Stickley dining table, #716, original finish, signed "The Work of..", excellent condition 3500-4500   May 19, 1996 Sold for $4750

210. L & JG Stickley dining table, #716, recent finish, signed "The Work of...", chip to edge, no leaves, very good condition   2000-3000 February 16, 1997   Sold for $2100

211. L & JG Stickley dining table, #713, round top over pedestal base with long corbels attached to a cruciform base, recent finish, some distress to top, branded, 48"dia. x 30"h, very good condition   2500-3500
December 3, 1995   Sold for $2000

212. L & JG Stickley chairs, set of six, four pictured, five sides, one armchair, three horizontal slats to back, drop-in spring cushion in new leather, original finish, branded "The Work of...", 18"w x 17"d x 37"h, excellent condition 3000-3500   March 3, 1996   Sold for $3500

213. L & JG Stickley table, #720, round top over five tapered legs, original leaves, original finish, branded, 48"dia. x 30"h, excellent condition   3500-4500   March 3, 1996   Sold for $3500

Not Pictured:

214. L & JG Stickley table, #722, round top with four leaves, legs drop down for expansion, cross-stretchers with corbelled center, original finish, Handcraft decal, 48"d x 29"h, excellent condition   1500-2000
November 17, 1992   Sold for $750

215. Roycroft dining chairs, #030 1/2, set of four, single wide vertical slat to back, recovered seat, recoated original finish, incised orb, 17"w x 17"d x 41"h, minor roughness, very good condition   1500-2000
November 14, 1993   Sold for $1500

216. Roycroft dining table, #0112, round table with four corbeled straight legs on a cruciform base, recent finish, incised orb, 48"d x 29"h, very good condition   2500-3500   November 14, 1993   Sold for $2600

217. Roycroft dining table, cross stretcher base with five legs, original finish, 54"square top, 31"h, two 11" leaves, excellent condition   4500-6500
September 30, 1990   Sold for $6000

218. Roycroft dining chairs, #27, set of seven, three are slightly different, replaced heavy leather seats, original finish, full signature, 18"w x 18"d x 38"h, excellent condition   2500-2500
September 30, 1990   Sold for $3200

219. Gustav Stickley dining chairs, two arm #354 1/2, two side #354, all branded, two arm & one side original finish, paper label, original leather, one side, some roughness & new leather, excellent condition   2000-2500
April 7, 1991   Sold for $3250

Not Pictured:

220. Gustav Stickley dining chairs, #354 1/2A, pair, original leather and tacks, cleaned original finish, red decal, excellent condition   1200-1500
May 2, 1993   Sold for $2400

221. Gustav Stickley dining chairs, #354 1/2, set of four, recent finish, original leather seats have been painted, most original tacks remain, paper label remnant, good condition   1500-2000
February 13, 1994   Sold for $2100

222. Gustav Stickley dining chairs, #354 1/2, pair, replaced leather seats, chip to bottom of one rear leg, stripped finish, branded signature, very good condition 700-900   February 13, 1994   Sold for $1100

223. Gustav Stickley dining chairs, #354, set of six, replaced leather seats, recent finish, some roughness, all in very good condition   3000-4000
September 30, 1990   Sold for $3750

224. Gustav Stickley dining chairs, #354, set of six, replaced hard leather seats, cleaned original finish, red decal and paper label, very good condition 4000-5000   March 3, 1996   Sold for $4750

225. Gustav Stickley dining chairs, #354, seven, original finish, red decal, excellent condition 4500-5500   November 24, 1996   Sold for $10,000

226. Gustav Stickley dining chairs, set of six, two #354A armchairs and four #354 side chairs, five vertical slats, original finish, red decal, new rush seats, armchairs 26"w x 21"d x 36"h, side chairs 19"w x 17"d x 36"h, excellent condition 4000-5000 October 23, 1994 Sold for $8000

Not Pictured:

227. Gustav Stickley dining chair, #354 1/2 A, worn original leather seat, original finish, red decal, chip to side rail, very good condition 500-700 October 23, 1994 Sold for $800

228. Gustav Stickley dining chair, #354 1/2, original hard leather seat and tacks, cleaned original finish, red decal, very good condition 600-800 May 19, 1996 Sold for $850

229. Gustav Stickley dining chairs, #312 1/2, set of six, five vertical slats in V-back, some with original finish, some with minor wood repairs, four signed, replaced leather and tacks to seats, 22"w x 18"d x 37"h, excellent condition 3500-4500 August 27, 1995 Sold for $4250

Not Pictured:

230. Gustav Stickley dining chairs, #312 1/2, set of six, fine original leather seats, two with minor tears, original finish, red decal and paper label, excellent condition 3500-4500 May 15, 1994 Sold for $6500

231. Gustav Stickley dining chair, #312 1/2, mahogany, replaced seat, original finish, red decal, very good condition 400-500 February 14, 1993 Sold for $700

232. Gustav Stickley dining chair, #312 1/2, mahogany, replaced seat, original finish, red decal, some roughness to front rail, good condition 300-400 February 14, 1993 Sold for $400

233. Gustav Stickley dining chair, #312 1/2, worn original leather seat, refinished, unsigned, very good condition 400-600 November 14, 1993 Sold for $500

234. Gustav Stickley armchair, #312 1/2, original leather seat has tear, original finish, red decal, very good condition 500-700 August 27, 1995 Sold for $900

235. Gustav Stickley armchair, #312 1/2, cleaned original finish, unsigned, very good condition 500-700 March 3, 1996 Sold for $450

236. Gustav Stickley dining chair, #312 1/2, replaced seat, original finish, red decal, very good condition 400-600 May 2, 1993 Sold for $800

237. Gustav Stickley dining chairs, #1301, set of six, three horizontal slats to back, new rush seat, fine original finish, red box mark, 18"w x 17"d x 38"h, excellent condition   3000-5000   March 3, 1996   Sold for $3250

Not Pictured:

238. Gustav Stickley dining chairs, #348, c.1904, set of eight ladderback chairs with original rush seats, rare slightly green finish occasionally used by Stickley on early examples, early box mark, 15.5"w x 15"d x 34.5"h, one chair has cracked leg, very good condition   2000-3000   April 7, 1991
Sold for $1500

239. Gustav Stickley dining chairs, #352, set of six chairs, four horizontal slats to back, top one arched, notched seat rail, drop-in seat with original oil cloth covering, original finish, red decal, 18"w x 16"d x 37"h, excellent condition   3500-4500   May 2, 1993
Sold for $6000

240. Gustav Stickley dining chairs, #2618, set of four, three horizontal slats to back, original leather covered seat has been removed but still intact, original finish, red box mark, 16"square x 35"h, very good condition   1500-2000   August 25, 1996
Sold for $1300

241. Gustav Stickley armchair, #310 1/2, three horizontal slats to back, replaced leather seat and tacks, original finish, branded, 25"w x 21"d x 36"h, very good condition   500-700   May 15, 1994
Sold for $550

242. Gustav Stickley armchairs, #310 1/2, pair, original hard leather seats with tacks, original finish, branded signature, paper label, excellent condition   1500-2000   December 3, 1995   Sold for $5500

243. Gustav Stickley dining chairs, #310 1/2, pair, original oil cloth and tacks on seat, cleaned original finish, red decal, has Eastwood paper label, some distress to back on one, very good condition   900-1200   March 3, 1996   Sold for $950

244. Gustav Stickley armchair, #310 1/2, original oil cloth and tacks on seat, cleaned original finish, red decal, very good condition   900-1200
May 19, 1996   Sold for $600

245. Gustav Stickley armchair, #310 1/2, original oilcloth and tacks on seat, cleaned original finish, red decal, very good condition   900-1200
May 19, 1996   Sold for $475

246. Gustav Stickley armchairs, #310 1/2, pair, original finish, signed with red decal, back of arm repaired on one, very good condition   900-1200
November 23, 1997   Sold for $850

247. Gustav Stickley dining chairs, #306 1/2, set of 6, original finish, burned mark, four with original leather, two have torn original leather, Eastwood labels, excellent condition   2000-3000   March 25, 1990   Sold for $3250

Not Pictured:

248. Gustav Stickley dining chair, #306 1/2, hard black leather seats, original finish, good condition 500-700   May 7, 1989   Sold for $550

249. Gustav Stickley dining chairs, #306 1/2, set of six, recent finish, very good condition   1500-2000 May 3, 1992   Sold for $950

250. Gustav Stickley dining chair, #306 1/2, replaced seat, original finish, red decal, very good condition 350-450   May 2, 1993   Sold for $220

251. Gustav Stickley dining chairs, #306 1/2, pair, new rush seats, recent finish, unsigned, very good condition   500-700   October 23, 1994 Sold for $425

252. Gustav Stickley dining chair, #306 1/2, recovered seat, original finish, branded, excellent condition 200-300   February 12, 1995   Sold for $325

253. Gustav Stickley dining chairs, #306 1/2, set of four, original hard leather seats, original finish, remnants of red decal and paper label, excellent condition 2000-2500   May 21, 1995   Sold for $3000

254. Gustav Stickley dining chairs, #306 1/2, set of six, original leather with tacks, original finish, branded signature and paper label, excellent condition 2000-2500   December 3, 1995   Sold for $3250

255. Gustav Stickley dining chair, #306 1/2, original leather seat and tacks, cleaned original finish, paper label, minor roughness to feet, very good condition 350-550   May 19, 1996   Sold for $325

256. Gustav Stickley dining chairs, #306, five sides and one arm, ladderback design with three slats to back, recovered brown leather seat, original finish, signed, excellent condition   2000-3000   February 16, 1997 Sold for $6000

257. Gustav Stickley dining chairs, set of five, four side chairs #306 1/2, one armchair #310 1/2, light ladder back with three horizontal slats to back, recovered seats, original finish, red decal, excellent condition 2000-2500   February 12, 1995   Sold for $2100

258. Gustav Stickley dining chairs, #1297, set of ten, eight side chairs, two arm chairs, early U-backs with four horizontal slats to back, drop-in seats, eight have original finish, red decals, side chairs 18"w x 16"d x 37"h, armchairs 23"w x 19"d x 40"h, very good to excellent condition   2500-3000 November 17, 1991   Sold for $4000

259. Gustav Stickley dining chairs, #349 1/2, set of six, three horizontal slats to back, original hard leather seat and tacks, fine original finish, red decal and paper label, 19"w x 17"d x 37"h, excellent condition 4000-6000   December 3, 1995   Sold for $5500

Not Pictured:

260. Gustav Stickley dining chairs, #349 1/2, pair, original leather seat and tacks, one torn, original finish, branded and paper label, very good condition 1000-1500   November 14, 1993   Sold for $2100

261. Gustav Stickley dining chairs, #349 1/2, pair, original hard leather seat and tacks, recent finish, signed red decal, very good condition   1200-1500 May 19, 1996   Sold for $1100

262. Gustav Stickley dining chairs, #349 1/2, pair, original leather seat and tacks, one with large tear, other with minor tear, original finish, branded and paper label, excellent condition   1200-1500 February 13, 1994   Sold for $2200

263. Gustav Stickley dining chairs, #1304, set of eight, two horizontal slats to back and original hard leather seat, V-shaped front seat rail, original finish, red box mark, 19"w x 16"d x 36"h, excellent condition 4500-6500   May 19, 1996   Sold for $5500

Not Pictured:

264. Gustav Stickley dining chairs, #1304A, pair of armchairs, original leather seat, original finish, red box mark, excellent condition   1500-2000 May 19, 1996   Sold for $2000

265. L & JG Stickley dining chairs, set of eight, six sides and two arms, five vertical slats with drop-in spring cushion, some original leatherette, some recovered, original finish, branded "The Work of...", two with Handcraft decal, armchair 27"w x 21"d x 36"h, side chair 21"w x 17"d x 36"h, chip on leg of one, excellent condition   6500-8500
May 21, 1995   Sold for $4250

266. L & JG Stickley dining chairs, one arm #B52, five side #950, all signed "The Work of...", original finish, some repairs, very good condition   1250-1500   April 7, 1991   Sold for $1400

267. Gustav Stickley
dining chairs,
#340 armchair
and #338 side
chairs, three side
chairs and one
armchair, drop-in
seats, original
finish, red decal,
armchair 24"w x
21"d x 40"h, side
16"w x 16"d x
39"h, excellent
condition
2000-3000
March 24, 1991
Sold for $2400

Not Pictured:

268. Gustav Stickley dining chairs, #338, pair, Harvey Ellis influence, three vertical slats to back, arched seat rail, refinished, repegged, unsigned, good condition   300-500   February 13, 1994 Sold for $375

269. Gustav Stickley dining chairs, #353, three sides and one arm, three slats to back and arched seat rail and slightly tapered legs, old leather seats, original finish, red decal, arm 25"w x 22"d x 41"h, excellent condition   2000-2500 December 3, 1995   Sold for $3500

270. Gustav Stickley dining chairs, #353, set of four, drop-in seats, original finish, branded, some roughness 1000-1500   May 3, 1992   Sold for $2000

271. Gustav Stickley dining chair, #353, original finish, numbered, red decal, excellent condition   400-500 May 21, 1995   Sold for $750

272. Gustav Stickley chairs, pair, #353, original finish, signed with red decal, very good condition 800-1100   November 23, 1997   Sold for $800

273. Gustav Stickley
dining chairs,
#370, set of six,
recent leather
drop-in seats, legs
taper at bottom,
recent finish,
unmarked,
excellent condition
1250-1750
March 27, 1988
Sold for $1700

Not Pictured:

274. Gustav Stickley dining chairs, #370, set of six, five side and one arm, original finish, recovered drop-in seat, all signed with decal, excellent condition 1500-2000   November 14, 1993   Sold for $2700

275. Gustav Stickley dining chairs, #308, set of four, recovered seats, H-backs, recent finish, unsigned, 17"w x 16"d x 40"h, good condition   900-1200 February 13, 1994   Sold for $1100

276. Gustav Stickley dining chair, #314, original leather, original finish, branded signature, excellent condition   600-800   February 12, 1995   Sold for $950

To buy, consign or sell these objects call:
(513) 321-6742 or (708) 383-5234

277. L & JG Stickley dining chairs, #804, set of six, five sides and one arm, two vertical slats to back, drop-in spring cushion, original finish, Handcraft signature, side chair 19"w x 18"d x 37"h, armchair 26"w x 21"d x 37"h, very good condition   1500-2000
May 21, 1995   Sold for $1600

278. L & JG Stickley drop leaf table, gate leg which opens to support rounded leaves and forms an oval top, original finish, Handcraft signature, open 64"w x 45"d x 30"h, very good condition   1000-1500
May 21, 1995   Sold for $1400

279. L & JG Stickley dining chairs, #341, five sides and one armchair, two horizontal slats to back, worn original oil cloth seat with original tacks on all but one, original finish, signed red Handcraft decal, 27"w x 21"d x 38"h, excellent condition 2500-3500
August 25, 1996 Sold for $1600

Not Pictured:

280. L & JG Stickley dining chairs, one #802 armchair, five #800 side chairs, drop-in cushion, original finish, unsigned, armchair 26"w x 20"d x 37"h, side chairs 18"w x 17"d x 37"h, very good condition 1500-2000   October 23, 1994   Sold for $2500

281. L & JG Stickley dining chairs, #800 and #802, five side chairs and one armchair, drop-in spring cushions, original finish, marked "The Work of...", excellent condition   1700-2200
November 15, 1992   Sold for $2400

282. L & JG Stickley dining chairs, #940, set of six, three vertical slats, wooden seat, original finish, decal "The Work of..", 18"w x 16"d x 36"h, very good condition   1500-2000   May 21, 1995
Sold for $2200

283. L & JG Stickley dining chairs, set of six, uncataloged, three slats to back, plank seats, original finish, Handcraft decal, 17"w x 16"d x 34"h, metal brackets added under legs, very good condition   800-1200
November 15, 1992   Sold for $700

284. Gustav Stickley vanity, #907, five drawers, large mirror with butterfly joints on harp, original finish, red decal and paper label, 48"w x 22"d x 55"h, excellent condition 3500-4500 March 24, 1991 Sold for $3000

285. Gustav Stickley vanity, #914, Harvey Ellis influence, two drawers with wooden knobs over arched apron, original mirror, original finish, red decal, 36"w x 18"d x 55"h, minor stains to top, very good condition 2000-3000 October 23, 1994 Sold for $2200

Not Pictured:

286. Gustav Stickley vanity, #914, original finish, signed with red decal, 36"w x 18"d x 54"h, excellent condition 2500-3500 November 23, 1997 Sold for $6000
Note: Same form as one pictured with iron hardware.

287. Gustav Stickley chest, #913, nine drawers with wood pulls, bowed sides, recent dark finish, red decal, 50"h x 36"w x 20"d, very good condition 5000-7000   September 24, 1989 Sold for $6250

Not Pictured:

288. Gustav Stickley chest, #913, original wooden knobs, original finish, red decal, paper label, excellent condition   7000-9000 December 3, 1995   Sold for $9000

289. Gustav Stickley chest, #913, wooden pulls, recent finish, red decal, several drawer bottoms replaced and some veneer damage to side, very good condition   4500-6500   February 16, 1997 Sold for $3500

290. Gustav Stickley dresser, #913, original V-pulls, original finish, branded signature, 36"w x 20"d x 51"h, excellent condition   8000-10,000 November 23, 1997   Sold for $14,000 **Note: Same form as one pictured with iron hardware.**

291. Gustav Stickley chest, #906, two drawers over four, full strap vertical copper hardware, panelled sides, original finish, red decal, 40"w x 21"d x 48"h, excellent condition 5000-7000   March 24, 1991 Sold for $6500

292. Gustav Stickley chest, #906, two drawers over four, iron pulls, paneled sides are mortised at bottom, recent finish, signed red decal, 40"w x 21"d x 45"h, excellent condition   4500-6500   March 27, 1988 Sold for $8250

293. Gustav Stickley chest, #626, two drawers over three, thru-tenon construction, iron oval pulls, original finish, Eastwood label, 36"w x 20"d x 43"h, excellent condition   4000-5000 November 17, 1991   Sold for $4500

Not Pictured:

294. Gustav Stickley chest, #626, recent finish, red decal, very good condition 3500-5000   October 4, 1987 Sold for $4000

295. Gustav Stickley chest, #626, facetted wooden knobs, unsigned, 43"h, very good condition   2000-2500 February 13, 1994   Sold for $2400

296. Gustav Stickley chest, #626, signed black decal, original finish, excellent condition   5500-7500 February 16, 1997   Sold for $8500

73

297. **Gustav Stickley** chest, #627, two half drawers over four large drawers, original oval copper hardware, inverted V-back and toe-board, thru-tenon construction and chamfered sides, original finish, signed with red decal, restoration to rear post, 40"w x 23"d x 53"h, very good condition   5000-7000   March 3, 1996   Sold for $7000

Not Pictured:

298. **Gustav Stickley** chest, #627, original finish, red decal, excellent condition   5000-7000   May 15, 1994   Sold for $6000

299. **Gustav Stickley** chest, #627, original finish, red decal, paper label, excellent condition   5000-6000   December 3, 1995   Sold for $9500

300. **Gustav Stickley** chest of drawers, #909, two half-drawers over three full drawers with original wood knobs, original finish, signed with red decal, 37"w x 19"d x 42"h, minor roughness, very good condition   2000-2500   August 24, 1997   Sold for $2600

301. **Gustav Stickley** chest, #902, two drawers over four with original brass oval pulls, paneled sides with thru-tenons, original finish, red decal, 42"w x 23"d x 54"h, excellent condition   8000-10,000   May 19, 1996 Sold for $16,000

Not Pictured:

302. **Gustav Stickley** chest, #902, two small drawers over four large, inverted V to galley top, chamfered sides, minor roughness, original finish, red decal, very good condition 3500-4500   May 3, 1992   Sold for $3250

303. Gustav Stickley stand, #642, two half drawers over one larger drawer with original wooden knobs, original finish to base, refinished top, red decal and paper label, 22"w x 16"d x 30"h, very good condition 1200-1700   December 3, 1995   Sold for $2300

304. Gustav Stickley chest, #909, two small drawers over three larger drawers with wooden knobs and paneled sides, original finish to base, top refinished, branded mark, 36"w x 20"d x 42"h, very good condition 1200-1700 December 3, 1995 Sold for $2400

Not Pictured:

305. Gustav Stickley chest, #909, light recoat over original finish, very clean, red decal and paper label, excellent condition   2500-3500 May 7, 1989   Sold for $1800

306. Gustav Stickley sewing cabinet, #630, two drawers with original copper ring pulls with two 10" drop-leaves, some cleaning to original finish, unsigned, 19"w x 18"d x 28"h, some separation and repair to top, very good condition   1500-1800 February 16, 1997   Sold for $1300

307. Gustav Stickley dresser, #905, full vertical strap iron hardware with circle pulls on two drawers over three, mirror with butterfly joints on posts, panelled sides with thru-tenons at bottom, original finish, red decal, 48"w x 23"d x 58"h, excellent condition   6000-8000 April 7, 1991   Sold for $15,000

Not Pictured:

308. Gustav Stickley dresser, #905, original finish, burned mark and paper label, excellent condition   5000-7000 September 30, 1990   Sold for $6600

309. Gustav Stickley dresser, #905, original finish, branded, excellent condition 4000-6000   May 3, 1992   Sold for $5500

310. Gustav Stickley dresser, #905, original finish, red decal, excellent condition 5000-6500   May 21, 1995   Sold for $7000

To buy, consign or sell these objects call:
(513) 321-6742 or (708) 383-5234

311. Gustav Stickley chest of drawers, #906, two drawers over four, full-strap iron pulls, mirror over chest with butterfly joints on posts, panelled sides and thru-tenons at bottom, original finish, branded signature and paper label, 72" to top of mirror, 40"w x 21"d, excellent condition   6000-8000
April 7, 1991 Sold for $20,000

312. Gustav Stickley dresser #911, two drawers over two, wood knobs arched skirt and bowed legs, butterfly joint in harp, original mirror, light recoat over original finish, very clean, 66"h x 45"w x 22"d, red decal and paper label, excellent condition   3500-4500   May 7, 1989
Sold for $2800

Not Pictured:

313. Gustav Stickley dresser, #911, original mirror, dresser top refinished, otherwise original finish, paper label and branded, very good condition   2000-3000
November 14, 1993   Sold for $2600

314. **Gustav Stickley** dresser, #911, Harvey Ellis influence, two short drawers over two large drawers above an arched toe-board with bowed sides, original mirror supported by harp frame with butterfly joint construction, recent finish, red decal, 48"w x 22"d x 68"h, very good condition 3000-3500   December 3, 1995   Sold for $3500
Note: Same form as preceding one but with different hardware.

Not Pictured:

315. **Gustav Stickley** dresser #911, original finish, red decal, excellent condition   2500-3500 August 27, 1995   Sold for $3750

316. **Gustav Stickley** dresser, #911, original iron V-pulls, original finish, signed with black decal, 48"w x 22"d x 67"h, excellent condition 4000-5000   November 23, 1997 Sold for $11,000

317. **Gustav Stickley** dresser, #625, two half drawers over two long drawers, original wood facetted pulls, thru-tenon construction and chamfered board at sides, original mirror, original finish, minor repair to drawer interior, very good condition   5000-7000 November 24, 1996   Sold for $4750

Not Pictured:

318. **Gustav Stickley** dresser, #625, two half drawers over two long drawers with wood facetted pulls, chamfered sides and thru-tenon construction, original mirror with copper candle holders on supports, signed large red decal, recent finish, 42"w x 22"d x 64"h, very good condition   4000-6000 May 4, 1997   Sold for $4250

319. Gustav Stickley bed, #923, full size with five wide slats under peaked top rail, splayed and tapered legs, cleaned original finish, red decal, headboard 59"w x 78"l x 48"h, very good condition 3500-4500   April 7, 1991 Sold for $10,000

Not Pictured:

320. Gustav Stickley bed, #923, original finish, red decal, excellent condition   4000-5000 November 14, 1993   Sold for $4250

321. Gustav Stickley bed, #923, original finish, branded signature, excellent condition   6000-8000 December 3, 1995   Sold for $4000

322. Gustav Stickley bed, #923, original finish, branded signature, minor restoration, 77"w x 57"d x 48"h, very good condition   4000-5000   May 4, 1997 Sold for $4500

323. Gustav Stickley inlaid bed, maple, with Arts & Crafts inlaid design in pewter and stained woods on top rail and bowed sides, paneled cane headboard, cleaned original finish, signed paper label, 46"w x 79"l x 40"h, height of bed has been shortened, very good condition   2000-2500 November 24, 1996 Sold for $2100

324. Gustav Stickley bed, #922, full-size bed with keyed tenons at top, horizontal slats over a wide horizontal board, original finish, red decal, 62"w x 79"l x 53"h, excellent condition 7000-9000
March 3, 1996
Sold for $6000

325. Gustav Stickley bed, #922, full-size bed, horizontal slat over wide horizontal board, slightly rounded top posts, original finish, branded signature, 59"w x 78"l x 58"h at headboard, excellent condition 6000-8000
May 21, 1995
Sold for $4250
Note: Same form as preceding one without the keyed tenons and slightly different dimensions.

326. Gustav Stickley double bed, footboard 37"h, headboard 49.5"h, 58"w, with original wooden rails, burned mark, original finish, excellent condition   2500-3500
March 25, 1990
Sold for $4000

Not Pictured:

327. Gustav Stickley double bed, burned mark, original finish, excellent condition   2500-3500
October 4, 1987
Sold for $3000

328. Gustav Stickley single bed, #923, arched top rail over three wide slats, splayed legs, branded signature, original finish, 75"l x 41"h, excellent condition   1500-2000   October 2, 1988
Sold for $1500

Not Pictured:

329. Gustav Stickley single bed, #923, original finish, red decal, very good condition   1200-1500
May 19, 1996 Sold for $800

330. Gustav Stickley bed, #917, heavy construction with three wide slats and attached slats to posts, original finish, signed with red decal, 58"w x 54"h x 80"l, excellent condition   7000-9000
November 23, 1997   Sold for $9500

331. Gustav Stickley child's bed, #919, spindled bed, slots in headboard to accommodate decorative fabric panel, original finish, red decal, 36"w x 56"l x 44"h, excellent condition   2500-3500 March 24, 1991 Sold for $4500

Not Pictured:

332. Gustav Stickley child's bed, #919, original cane has some breaks, original finish, red decal, very good condition 3000-4000 November 15, 1992 Sold for $3500

333. Gustav Stickley child's wardrobe, #920, iron V-pulls on panelled doors, arched apron, one interior drawer is replaced, original finish, paper label, 33"w x 16.5"d x 60"h, very good condition 2500-3500   September 30, 1990   Sold for $4675

334. Gustav Stickley wardrobe, similar in design to child's wardrobe #920, but custom size, two shelf interior, original finish, decal, 45"w x 16"d x 70"h, excellent condition   3500-4500
November 15, 1992   Sold for $3500

335. Gustav Stickley wardrobe, similar to #920, but larger with hooks and clothing pole inside, original finish, brown decal, 36"w x 16"d x 70"h, very good condition 2000-3000   May 3, 1992   Sold for $3500

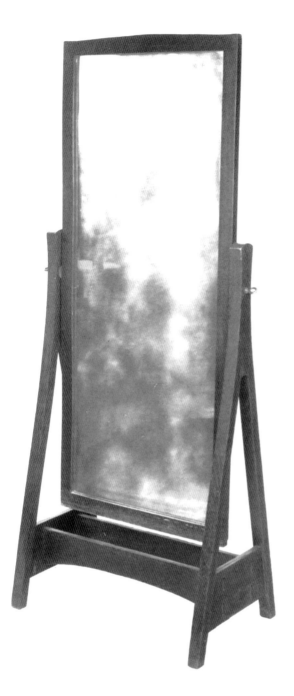

336. Gustav Stickley Cheval mirror, #918, influenced by Harvey Ellis with bowed legs and arched thru-tenon double stretchers, slight arch to mirror frame, original mirror, original finish, red decal, 30"w x 17"d x 70"h, some wear to bottom of feet, very good condition 5500-7500   December 3, 1995   Sold for $6500

Not Pictured:

337. Gustav Stickley Cheval mirror, #918, original glass, original finish, brown decal, excellent condition 5000-7000   May 3, 1992   Sold for $8500

338. Gustav Stickley Cheval mirror, #918, original finish, red decal, wear to one foot, excellent condition   6500-8500 August 24, 1997   Sold for $7000

339. Gustav Stickley stand, #641, two drawers under square top with backsplash, tapered legs, original finish, red decal, 20"square top x 31"h, excellent condition   1000-1500   October 23, 1994 Sold for $1900

Not Pictured:

340. Gustav Stickley stand, #641, black ink stamp mark, recent finish, very good condition   900-1200 April 7, 1991   Sold for $1300

341. Gustav Stickley stand, #641, original finish, red decal and paper label, excellent condition 1200-1500   November 14, 1993   Sold for $1400

342. Gustav Stickley stand, #641, original finish, red decal, some distress to top, very good condition 1000-1500   December 3, 1995   Sold for $1300

343. L & JG Stickley dresser, #101, three small drawers over two larger drawers with original wooden knobs, mirror with arched top, original finish, signed "The Work of...", 45"w x 21"d x 67"h, excellent condition 2000-2500   August 27, 1995   Sold for $1900

Not Pictured:

344. L & JG Stickley dresser, two drawers over two, arched apron, panelled sides, slight arch to mirror top, wood knobs, original finish, unsigned, 42"w x 21"d x 67"h, excellent condition   1000-1500 November 15, 1992   Sold for $1200

345. L & JG Stickley dressing table, #87, two drawers with original wooden knobs over a recessed lower shelf, paneled sides, swivel mirror, original finish, Handcraft decal, scratch to top, 44"w x 22"d x 55"h, very good condition   2000-2500   May 4, 1997 Sold for $1700

346. L & JG Stickley dresser, #81, three drawers over two, wooden knobs, original frame and glass, original finish with minor stains, unsigned, 44"w x 21"d x 67"h, very good condition 1200-1500 November 14, 1993 Sold for $1600

347. L & JG Stickley stand, #105, two drawers with wooden knobs, original finish, unsigned, 20"w x 14"d x 30"h, excellent condition 900-1200 November 14, 1993 Sold for $1000

348. L & JG Stickley chiffonier, #102, two cabinets above four drawers, wooden knobs, original finish, unsigned, 36"w x 18"d x 50"h, excellent condition 2000-3000 November 14, 1993 Sold for $2700

349. L & JG Stickley chest, #94, nine drawers with wood knobs, cleaned original finish, Handcraft decal, some restoration, 32"w x 19"d x 53"h, very good condition 3500-4500 February 16, 1997 Sold for $3750

Not Pictured:

350. L & JG Stickley chest, #90, two half drawers over four full drawers with arched toe-board, paneled sides, cleaned original finish, Handcraft decal, replaced hardware, 34"w x 20"d x 53"h, very good condition 1000-1500 November 24, 1996 Sold for $1500

351. **L & JG Stickley** chiffonier, #111, chest with two paneled doors concealing interior drawers with original hardware, some work has been done to doors, 48"h x 40"w x 19"d, very good condition   4000-5000 March 27, 1988 Sold for $2900

352. **L & JG Stickley** wardrobe, paneled cabinet has one door which conceals an open interior with a hanging rod, arched bottom, branded "The Work of....", cleaned original finish, lock is missing, replaced pull, 26"w x 21"d x 74"h, very good condition   2000-3000   May 15, 1994 Sold for $2200

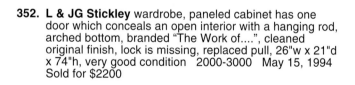

353. L & JG Stickley bed, #92, tall tapered posts separated by seven slats with wider center slat, original finish, signed, 58"w x 44"h, excellent condition 6500-8500 May 19, 1996 Sold for $10,000

354. L & JG Stickley bed, #92, single, one wide slat center of each end with two smaller slats on either side, great original finish, decal mark, "The Work of …", 80"l, 50"h headboard, 44"h foot, 46"w, rails held with pegs, excellent condition 3000-3500 May 7, 1989 Sold for $2600

Not Pictured:

355. L & JG Stickley bed, single bed with five slats to headboard and footboard, refinished, branded signature, very good condition 900-1200 May 19, 1996 Sold for $325

To buy, consign or sell these objects call: (513) 321-6742 or (708) 383-5234

356. L & JG Stickley bed, #83, three quarter size, arched apron under framed double panel construction centered between tapered posts, footboard and headboard join rails via removable pegs, 46"w x 51"h headboard, 46"w x 45"h footboard, minor nicks and wear, excellent condition   2000-3000
February 12, 1995   Sold for $2000

357. Roycroft dressing table, #110, Macmurdo feet, Roycroft orb on right leg, adjustable mirror, original finish, copper pulls, 56"h x 39"w x 17.5"d, excellent condition 2000-3000   September 30, 1990
Sold for $2750

358. Roycroft dresser, #108, MacMurdo feet, two over two drawers, beveled mirror, copper hardware, original finish, script signature, 45"w x 26"d x 61"h, excellent condition   3000-4000 November 15, 1992   Sold for $2900

Not Pictured:

359. Roycroft dresser, #108, script signature, original finish, excellent condition   3000-4000 September 30, 1990   Sold for $3250

360. Roycroft vanity, center mirror with two hinged side mirrors above dressing table with one center drawer and two short drawers on each side, cleaned original finish, orb mark, 53"w x 24"d x 58"h, replaced hardware, very good condition   2000-2500 February 12, 1995   Sold for $1800

361. **Roycroft** twin bed #0106, MacMurdo feet, eight slats to headboard and footboard, original box springs have "Roycroft" woven into piping, recent finish, headboard with orb, headboard 45"w x 58"h, footboard 45"w x 34"h x 80"l, very good condition   1000-2000 May 3, 1992 Sold for $2400

362. **Roycroft** dresser, #0109, two small drawers over two larger ones, copper hardware, recent finish, orb on bottom drawer, 44"w x 26"d x 40"h; with **Roycroft** mirror (not pictured), beveled glass, candle sconces and hanging chains missing, 42"w x 34"h, both very good condition 1500-2000   May 3, 1992 Sold for $1500

Not Pictured:

363. **Roycroft** twin bed, #0106, recent finish, headboard with orb, very good condition   1000-2000 May 3, 1992   Sold for $2400

364. **Roycroft** dresser, #0109, copper hardware, recent finish, orb on bottom drawer, with Roycroft mirror, hanging chains missing, both very good condition 1500-2000   May 3, 1992   Sold for $1500

365. **Charles Stickley** chest of drawers, attribution, has two drawers over four, wooden pulls, inverted V-gallery and chamfered sides, original finish, 38"w x 20"d x 55"h, excellent condition   1500-2000 November 14, 1993   Sold for $2300

366. Gustav Stickley
mirror, #66, four iron coat hooks, original finish, gentle arch to top, 28" x 36", red decal, excellent condition   1500-2500
March 27, 1988
Sold for $2300

367. Gustav Stickley mirror, #68, three sections, four iron hooks, paper label, large red decal, recent finish, 48"w x 28"h, very good condition   2250-2750
October 2, 1988   Sold for $1500

368. Gustav Stickley mirror, #608, rectangular mirror with thru-tenon construction, original plate glass mirror, copper candle sconces added later, cleaned original finish, unsigned, 42"w x 29"h, very good condition   1500-2000
February 13, 1994   Sold for $1500

369. Gustav Stickley mirror, wishbone holds arched frame, base on four round feet, cleaned original finish, 26"w x 20"h, signed with red decal, very good condition   1500-2000
May 19, 1996   Sold for $1800

370. L & JG Stickley hall mirror, peaked top and corbeled, four original hammered hooks, original mirror and chain, original finish, "The Work of ...", 40"w x 24"h, excellent condition   1500-2000   May 15, 1994   Sold for $2300

Not Pictured:

371. L & JG Stickley mirror, #100, arched top and bottom, original glass and hardware, original finish, unsigned, 45"w x 26"h, excellent condition   1500-2000   August 24, 1997   Sold for $2000

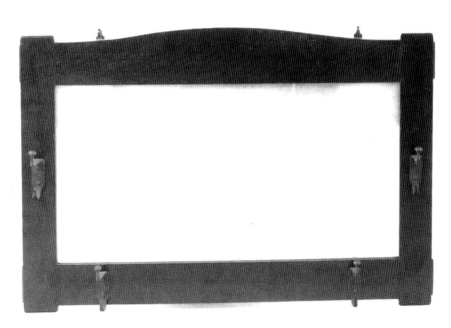

372. L & JG Stickley hall mirror, #65, curved top with thru-tenon construction, four iron hooks, cleaned original finish, signed "The Work of...", 40"w x 27"h, very good condition   1500-2000   May 21, 1995   Sold for $2500

Arts & Crafts Furniture
Reference Book

373. Gustav Stickley settle, #173, thirteen slats to a canted back with four slats under canted arm, heavy post construction, replaced rope foundation, recovered original cushions, recoated original finish, unsigned, 71"w x 29"d x 39"h, very good condition
9000-12,000   November 24, 1996   Sold for $8500

374. Gustav Stickley settle, #222, tall tapered posts and twenty-two slats to back with eight slats under even arm, replaced drop-in spring cushion, original finish, red decal, 80"w x 32"d x 37"h, excellent condition
12,000-17,000   May 19, 1996   Sold for $15,000

375. Gustav Stickley
settle, #206, tall tapered posts with seven wide slats to back and three on each side, rope foundation, original finish, red decal, 60"w x 28"d x 40"h, excellent condition
10,000-12,000
March 27, 1988
Sold for $20,000

Not Pictured:

376. Gustav Stickley settle, #206, original finish, large red decal, excellent condition 7000-9000
May 15, 1994 Sold for $9000

377. Gustav Stickley settle, #206, original finish, large red decal, excellent condition 10,000-12,000
December 3, 1995 Sold for $12,000

378. Gustav Stickley settle, #208, even arm with thru-tenon construction, three slats under arms and eight to back, recent finish, branded signature, 77"w x 32"d x 29"h, replaced seat, very good condition
5500-7500 March 3, 1996 Sold for $7000

Not Pictured:

379. Gustav Stickley settle, #208, recent finish, burned mark, excellent condition 9000-10,000
March 27, 1988 Sold for $11,550

380. Gustav Stickley settle, #208, cleaned original finish, inset cushion, very good condition
5000-7000 February 14, 1993 Sold for $8000

381. Gustav Stickley settle, #208, recoated original finish, conjoined label, very good condition
5500-6500 October 23, 1994 Sold for $6000

382. Gustav Stickley settle, #208, drop-in spring cushion, recent finish, branded signature, very good condition
6500-8500 August 25, 1996 Sold for $7000

383. Gustav Stickley settle, #208, recovered original spring cushion, fine original finish, unsigned, 77"w x 32"d x 29"h, excellent condition 6000-8000
February 16, 1997 Sold for $6000

384. Gustav Stickley settle, #226, even arm settle with five slats under each arm, wide back rail, spring cushion, original finish, 60"w x 31"d x 29"h, very good condition 5000-7000 November 15, 1992 Sold for $5500

Not Pictured:

385. Gustav Stickley settle, #226, original finish, new leather cushion and seat, branded, excellent condition 5000-6000 February 13, 1994 Sold for $7000

386. Gustav Stickley settle, #225, five wide slats under even arms with a wide horizontal board to back, recent finish, veneer repairs and loss, original leatherette cushions, 78"w x 31"d x 29"h, very good condition 3500-4500 February 12, 1995 Sold for $5500

Not Pictured:

387. Gustav Stickley settle, #225, cushions and seat covers with top quality leather, original finish cleaned, red decal, excellent condition 10,000-12,500 May 7, 1989 Sold for $5800

388. Gustav Stickley settle, #225, original finish cleaned, early rope seat with cane support, leather cushions, red decal, excellent condition 7500-9500 March 25, 1990 Sold for $6500

389. Gustav Stickley settle, #225, recovered original cushion, original finish, red decal, 78"w x 31"d x 29"h, excellent condition 7000-9000 May 4, 1997 Sold for $6000

390. Gustav Stickley settle, #225, recovered original spring cushion, original finish, signed with red decal, minor veneer repairs to feet, very good condition 5500-6500 November 23, 1997 Sold for $4750

391. Gustav Stickley hall settle, #205, wide slats across back and under arms, thru-tenons top and bottom, leather covered seat cushion, recent finish, 56"l x 22"d x 30"h excellent condition 2500-3500 March 27, 1988 Sold for $2900

Not Pictured:

392. Gustav Stickley hall settle, #205, original drop-in frame with replaced rope foundation and loose cushion, caning missing, recent finish, unsigned, very good condition 1500-2000 February 12, 1995 Sold for $2200

393. Gustav Stickley settle, #172, keyed thru-tenon on stretcher at bottom, recent finish, reupholstered, 56"w x 21"d x 33"h, very good condition 2000-3000 October 2, 1988 Sold for $2150

Not Pictured:

394. Gustav Stickley settle, #172, leather upholstered back and seat over a horizontal stretcher with keyed tenon construction, original leather and tacks, original finish, unsigned, some repaired tears to back, very good condition 4500-5500 May 4, 1997 Sold for $3500

395. Gustav Stickley hall bench, #219, seventeen back slats, open arm with corbels, branded signature, original finish, 72"w x 26"d x 38"h, repair to back, some roughness, very good condition   1750-2250   May 15, 1994   Sold for $1600

396. Gustav Stickley settee, #212, twelve slats to back, original hard leather seat and tacks, light recoat over original finish, red decal, 47"w x 25"d x 36"h, very good condition 2000-3000   December 3, 1995 Sold for $2400

Not Pictured:

397. Gustav Stickley settee, #212, re-placed leather seat, recent finish, some roughness, good condition   800-1000 November 15, 1992 Sold for $1300

398. Gustav Stickley settee, #212, original hard leather and tacks, original finish, red decal, excellent condition   2000-3000 February 12, 1995 Sold for $3750

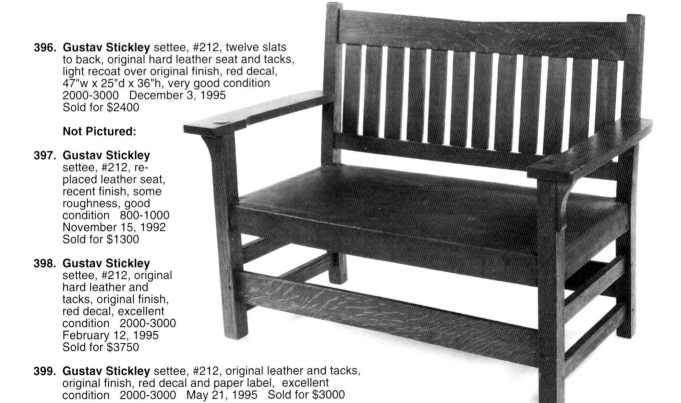

399. Gustav Stickley settee, #212, original leather and tacks, original finish, red decal and paper label,   excellent condition   2000-3000   May 21, 1995   Sold for $3000

400. Gustav Stickley settee, #212, original worn leather seat, original finish, red decal, very good condition   1500-2000   August 27, 1995   Sold for $1700

401. Gustav Stickley settee, #212, recovered leather cushion, original tacks, recent finish, unsigned, 48"w x 25"d x 36"h, very good condition   1500-2000   May 4, 1997 Sold for $1500

To buy, consign or sell these objects call:
(513) 321-6742 or (708) 383-5234

402. Gustav Stickley settle, #161, four horizontal slats to back with arch to top, thick drop arm and loose cushion rest on original framed foundation, recent finish, unsigned, 50"w x 27"d x 38"h, very good condition   1500-2000
February 13, 1994
Sold for $1800

403. Gustav Stickley hall seat, #224, with cut-outs on sides, paneled back and lift seat above storage area, thru-tenon construction, original finish, branded, 48"w x 22"d x 42"h, excellent condition
4000-5000
November 14, 1993
Sold for $3500

Not Pictured:

404. Gustav Stickley hall seat, #224, original finish, branded signature, excellent condition
5500-6500   May 21, 1995
Sold for $9000

405. Gustav Stickley daybed, #220, a knockdown bed with six slats at head and foot, new cushions and cushion frame, red decal, 82"l x 36"d x 34"h, original finish
6000-8000   March 25, 1990
Sold for $4500

Not Pictured:

406. Gustav Stickley daybed, #220, new cushions and cushion frame, red decal, original finish, excellent condition
3500-4500   May 2, 1993   Sold for $5000

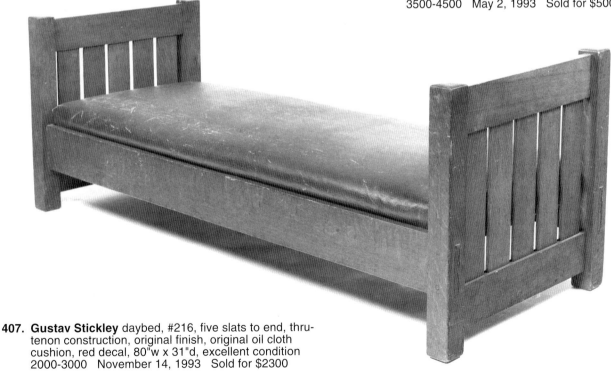

407. Gustav Stickley daybed, #216, five slats to end, thru-tenon construction, original finish, original oil cloth cushion, red decal, 80"w x 31"d, excellent condition
2000-3000   November 14, 1993   Sold for $2300

Not Pictured:

408. Gustav Stickley daybed, #216, loose cushion supported by replaced cane, original finish, very good condition
3000-4000   November 17, 1991   Sold for $2100

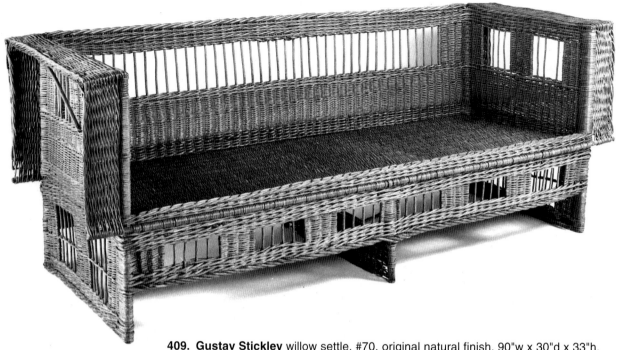

409. Gustav Stickley willow settle, #70, original natural finish, 90"w x 30"d x 33"h, three missing spindles on sides, very good condition   3000-5000
November 15, 1992   Sold for $3750

410. L & JG Stickley settle, #221, tall tapered posts, sixteen slats to back, seven slats to each side, original leatherette has tears, original finish, red decal, 60"w x 30"d x 39"h, excellent condition   9000-12,000   May 2, 1993   Sold for $7500

411. L & JG Stickley settle, from Onondaga Shops, even arms over four slats and fifteen slats to back with interior corbels on four tapered posts, original cane foundation, original loose cushions with some loss to original leather, original finish, 72"w x 26"d x 39"h, excellent condition   10,000-15,000   May 21, 1995   Sold for $9500

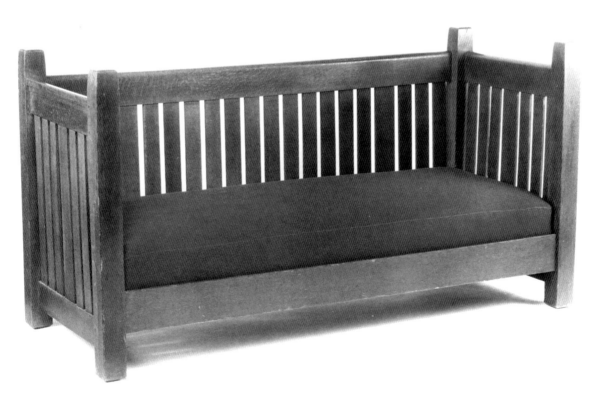

412. L & JG Stickley settle, #223, tall tapered posts, twenty-two slats to back, seven slats to each side, original spring cushion recently covered in brown leather, original finish, Handcraft decal, 84"w x 32"d x 39"h, excellent condition 7000-9000   May 3, 1992   Sold for $11,000

413. L & JG Stickley settle, #222, even arm with seven slats under arm, middle slat is wider, twenty slats to back, slightly canted back and sides, original leather cushion and pillows, original finish, signed "The Work of...", 76"w x 31"d x 39"h, excellent condition   12,000-17,000
August 25, 1996   Sold for $13,000

Not Pictured:

414. L & JG Stickley settle, #222, recovered original cushion, original finish, handcraft decal, excellent condition   7000-9000
November 17, 1991   Sold for $9000

415. L & JG Stickley settle, #281, capped arms and back, beveled edge on front seat support, original finish, spring cushion covered in worn original leather, signed with decal "The Work of ...", 76"l x 34"h x 31"d, excellent condition   7500-9500
March 24, 1991   Sold for $6500

Not Pictured:

416. L & JG Stickley settle, #281, original spring cushion, original finish, signed "The Work of...", minor separation to post, excellent condition   7000-9000   December 3, 1995   Sold for $7000

417. L & JG Stickley settle, #281, recovered cushion, Handcraft decal, original finish, 77"w x 31"d x 34"h, excellent condition   7000-9000   August 24, 1997   Sold for $7000

418. L & JG Stickley settle, #280, even arms with beveled posts, twelve slats to back, five slats under each arm, recent finish, marked "The Work of ...", 60"w x 31"d x 34"h, very good condition   2500-3500   February 14, 1993 Sold for $4750   **Note: Same form as preceding one, but more narrow.**

Not Pictured:

420. L & JG Stickley settle, #232, original finish, Handcraft decal, excellent condition   2000-3000 November 14, 1993   Sold for $3250

419. L & JG Stickley settle, #232, one wide slat to sides and five wide slats to back, recovered original cushion, original finish, branded signature, 72"w x 27"d x 28"h, excellent condition   4500-6500 May 19, 1996   Sold for $4250

421. L & JG Stickley settle, #232, replaced cushion, original finish, Handcraft decal, very good condition 3500-5500   August 25, 1996   Sold for $3750

422. L & JG Stickley settle, #232, recovered original spring cushion, recent finish, branded, some roughness, good condition   2500-3500 August 24, 1997   Sold for $2200

423. L & JG Stickley settle, #229, wide horizontal board to back, two vertical slats to each side with tapered posts, nicely recovered leather cushion, refinished, unsigned, 71"w x 26"d x 35"h, very good condition 4000-5000   February 16, 1997   Sold for $3000

Not Pictured:

424. L & JG Stickley settle, similar to #229, single wide horizontal slat across back with two slats on side, original finish, Handcraft decal, 66"w x 26"d x 35"h, excellent condition   3500-4500   November 14, 1993   Sold for $2600

425. L & JG Stickley settle, #285, even arms with two slats under each and seven wide slats to back, arched front rail pulls out to make a 3/4 bed, original finish, signed "The Work of...", 70"w x 27"d x 34"h, excellent condition   5000-7000 November 24, 1996   Sold for $5500

426. L & JG Stickley settle, #215, even arm with two slats under arm and seven slats to back, restrung foundation, recovered cushion, original finish, Handcraft decal, 72"w x 26"d x 36"h, excellent condition   3500-4500
February 12, 1995   Sold for $4000

427. L & JG Stickley settle, #263, two slats under a bent arm, seven slats to back under an arched top rail, original cushion, signed "The Work of....", original finish, 77"w x 29"d x 37"h, excellent condition 3500-4500   May 15, 1994   Sold for $5500

Not Pictured:

428. L & JG Stickley settle, #225, thirteen slats to back under a notched top rail, recovered original drop-in spring cushion, original finish, Handcraft decal, 53"w x 23"d x 37"h, very good condition 1500-2000   August 25, 1996   Sold for $1700

429. L & JG Stickley settle, #225, original leather drop-in spring cushion, some tears to leather, recent finish, repair to one arm, some roughness to other arm, unsigned, very good condition   1500-2000
May 19, 1996   Sold for $1200

430. L & JG Stickley settle, similar to #206, thirteen vertical slats to back, wooden seat, recent finish, some roughness, unsigned, 68"w x 22"d x 37"h, good condition   900-1200   May 19, 1996
Sold for $800

431. L & JG Stickley settle, #225, recovered original cushion, original finish, Handcraft decal, 53"w x 24"d x 36"h, very good condition   1500-1800
May 4, 1997   Sold for $1300

To buy, consign or sell these objects call:
(513) 321-6742 or (708) 383-5234

432. L & JG Stickley settle,
Onondaga Shops, original
leather back and seat, 41.5"h
x 40.5"w, original finish, paper
label, excellent condition
700-900   October 4, 1987
Sold for $1200

433. L & JG Stickley daybed, #922, Onondaga Shops, vertical head-
rest having three wide slats and eight slats beneath each side,
replaced cushion, refinished, unsigned, 72"w x 27"d x 28"h, very
good condition   3000-4000   November 24, 1996   Sold for $2500

Not Pictured:

434. L & JG Stickley daybed, #295, angled form with
five slats to head and foot, refinished, conjoined
label, 72"w x 28"d x 22"h, very good condition
800-1000   October 23, 1994   Sold for $950

435. L & JG Stickley daybed, #292, four vertical slats between angled posts with thru-tenons, replaced fabric on original cushion, Handcraft decal, some color added to original finish, 80"w x 30"d x 28"h, very good condition   2500-3500 February 13, 1994   Sold for $2800

Not Pictured:

436. L & JG Stickley daybed, #292, original finish, spring cushion reupholstered in green leather, excellent condition   3500-5000   May 7, 1989 Sold for $5200

437. L & JG Stickley daybed, #292, original spring cushion, original finish, signed " The Work of...", excellent condition   2500-3500   December 3, 1995 Sold for $3000

438. Charles Stickley drop arm settle, thru-tenons, attribution, five slats under arms, fourteen slats in back, 76"w x 33"d x 35"h, original finish, excellent condition 2500-3500   April 7, 1991   Sold for $3000

Arts & Crafts Furniture
Reference Book

439. Gustav Stickley Morris chair, #369, five vertical slats under arms, thru-tenons, cleaned original finish, red decal, 24" seat width x 40"h, minor repair under one arm in back, very good condition   4000-5000   November 15, 1992 Sold for $5000

Not Pictured:

440. Gustav Stickley Morris chair, #369, spring cushion, original finish, new green leather cushions, large red decal, one peg for recliner is new, excellent condition   5500-7000   May 7, 1989 Sold for $7250

441. Gustav Stickley Morris chair, #369, replaced pegs, original spring cushion recovered in canvas, recoat over original finish, red decal, very good condition 5000-7000   September 30, 1990   Sold for $8000

442. Gustav Stickley Morris chair, #369, replaced cushions in green leather, nicely refinished, red decal, minor veneer repair, very good condition 4500-5500   October 23, 1994   Sold for $6000

443. Gustav Stickley Morris chair, #369, cleaned original finish, minor restoration, branded signature, very good condition   5500-6500   May 21, 1995 Sold for $8000

444. Gustav Stickley Morris chair, #369, cleaned and recoated original light finish, unsigned, very good condition   7000-9000   May 19, 1996 Sold for $8000

445. Gustav Stickley Morris chair, #369, recovered cushions, two back pegs replaced, original finish, branded signature, 33"w x 38"d x 38"h, excellent condition   9000-12,000   August 24, 1997 Sold for $12,000

446. Gustav Stickley Morris chair, #332, five slats under arm and adjustable back with original facetted pegs, replaced rope foundation, original finish, signed with red decal under arm, minor chips to one arm, 32"w x 38"d x 40"h, excellent condition   5500-7500   November 24, 1996   Sold for $8500

Not Pictured:

447. Gustav Stickley Morris chair, #332, recent leather cushions, original finish, burned mark, excellent condition   2400-2700   October 4, 1987   Sold for $3500

448. Gustav Stickley Morris chair, #332, early rope seat, recent leather cushions, original finish, paper label, very good condition   4000-5000   October 2, 1988   Sold for $4100

449. Gustav Stickley Morris chair, #332, original finish has been cleaned, recent leather cushions, excellent condition   4500-5500   April 7, 1991   Sold for $4250

450. Gustav Stickley Morris chair, #332, original finish, red decal, excellent condition   4000-5000   May 3, 1992   Sold for $4000

451. Gustav Stickley Morris chair, #332, recent leather cushions on original cane support, original finish, red decal, excellent condition   5000-6000   February 14, 1993   Sold for $5000

452. Gustav Stickley Morris chair, #332, recovered with Schumacher fabric, original finish, branded, very good condition   4000-5000   May 2, 1993   Sold for $4500

453. Gustav Stickley Morris chair, #332, original finish, recovered leather cushions, branded signature, excellent condition   4500-5500   May 15, 1994   Sold for $5500

454. Gustav Stickley Morris chair, #332, original finish, minor veneer repair, branded, very good condition   4000-5000   October 23, 1994   Sold for $5000

455. Gustav Stickley Morris chair, #346, original finish, red decal, 30"w x 33"d x 42"h, excellent condition   1200-1500   March 25, 1990   Sold for $2250

456. Gustav Stickley Morris chair, #346, open arms, adjustable back, new cushion, original finish, red decal, some roughness, good condition   1200-1700   May 21, 1995   Sold for $1700

457. Gustav Stickley Morris chair, #346, spring seat cushion, recent finish, unsigned, one peg missing, very good condition   1000-1500   March 3, 1996   Sold for $1000

458. Gustav Stickley Morris chair, #346, cushions in brown leather, original finish, red decal, 31"w x 34"d x 42"h, excellent condition   2000-2500   May 4, 1997   Sold for $2000

459. Gustav Stickley Morris chair, #319, open under arm with adjustable back and original worn leather drop-in cushion, replaced pegs, recoated original finish, overall roughness red decal, 31"w x 34"d x 39"h, good condition   900-1200   February 16, 1997   Sold for $1100

460. Gustav Stickley Morris chair, #2340, early form with narrow arms over reverse-tapered legs and original facetted pegs, upholstered in hi-grade leather, recent finish, unsigned, 29"w x 33"d x 39"h, very good condition 5500-6500   May 15, 1994
Sold for $6500   **Note: This chair is different than the 336 bow arm. The legs flare and are larger at the bottom.**

Not Pictured:

461. Gustav Stickley Morris chair, #2340, reversed tapered legs, original faceted pegs, light recoat over original finish, unsigned, very good condition 7000-9000   February 16, 1997
Sold for $8000

462. Gustav Stickley Morris chair, #2340, in ash, recovered cushions, unsigned, recent finish, 29"w x 33"d x 38"h, very good condition   5000-7000
November 23, 1997   Sold for $6500

463. Gustav Stickley Morris chair, #336, arched seat support and replaced cane foundation, original facetted pegs, lightly recoated original finish, marked with red decal, 30"w x 36"d x 39"h, excellent condition   7000-9000
August 27, 1995   Sold for $11,000

Not Pictured:

464. Gustav Stickley Morris chair, #336, recent finish, no mark, very good condition   3500-4500
October 2, 1988   Sold for $3100

465. Gustav Stickley Morris chair, #336, replaced cushions, recent finish, very good condition 3500-5000   February 14, 1993
Sold for $4250

466. Gustav Stickley Morris chair, #336, original rope foundation, recent finish, box mark, one peg replaced, very good condition   4000-5000
February 13, 1994   Sold for $5000

467. Gustav Stickley Morris chair, #336, original cane foundation missing, cleaned finish, some veneer repair, unsigned, very good condition   4000-5000
August 27, 1995   Sold for $5500

468. Gustav Stickley Morris chair, #336, one facetted peg broken, recent finish, arms altered at back, good condition   3500-4500   August 25, 1996
Sold for $3750

469. Gustav Stickley Morris chair, #336, original cane foundation, original finish, three replaced pegs, excellent condition   9000-12,000   August 25, 1996
Sold for $12,000

470. Gustav Stickley Morris chair, #336, recovered leather cushions, unsigned, recent finish, 30"w x 36"d x 44"h, very good condition   5000-7000
May 4, 1997   Sold for $4750

471. **Gustav Stickley** Morris chair, #2341, early form with two slats and interior corbels under each arm, original wrapped leather at front and back, original tacks at front, seat frame altered, original finish, 29"w x 34"d x 38"h, very good condition
7000-9000   August 25, 1996   Sold for $8000

Not Pictured:

472. **Gustav Stickley** Morris chair, #2341, original sling seat, recent finish, unsigned, very good condition
4000-5000   November 23, 1997
Sold for $3000

473. **Gustav Stickley** Morris chair, #334, original finish, red decal, excellent condition   3500-4500
November 14, 1993   Sold for $6000
Note: Chair #334 is almost identical to #2341 only a few years later.

474. **Gustav Stickley** Morris chair, #334, original sling set, original finish, red decal, excellent condition
4000-5000   February 12, 1995
Sold for $7000

475. **Gustav Stickley** Morris chair, #334, replaced canvas foundation, original pegs, decal, recent finish, very good condition   4500-6500   May 19, 1996
Sold for $3500

476. **Gustav Stickley** Morris chair, #334, replaced leather seat foundation with copper tacks front and back, original pegs, 1904 decal, recent finish, unsigned, very good condition
5000-6000   May 19, 1996
Sold for $3750

477. **Gustav Stickley** Morris chair, #367, seventeen spindles under flat arms, original sling seat, minor repairs, recent finish, unsigned, 30"w x 36"d x 39"h, very good condition   4000-5000
May 21, 1995   Sold for $6500

Not Pictured:

478. **Gustav Stickley** Morris chair, #367, sixteen spindles, recent finish, very good condition
7500-10,000   October 2, 1988
Sold for $7000

479. **Gustav Stickley** Morris chair, #367, sixteen spindles, original finish, minor height loss, very good condition   4500-6500
May 19, 1996   Sold for $4000

480. **Gustav Stickley** Morris chair, #367, seventeen spindles, recoat over original finish, paper label, very good condition   7000-9000
August 25, 1996   Sold for $7500

481. Gustav Stickley Morris chair, #367, eighteen spindles, replaced canvas sling seat, partial original finish, replaced pegs, 40"h, excellent condition   9000-11,000
October 4, 1987   Sold for $11,550
Note: This chair differs from the preceding chair in that it has eighteen spindles rather than sixteen or seventeen.

482. Gustav Stickley Morris chair, #367, twenty-two spindles under flat arms, original canvas sling seat, enhanced original finish, signed with Eastwood paper label, very good condition 8000-11,000
March 25, 1990
Sold for $7500   **Note: This chair differs from the chairs preceding it because it has twenty-two spindles.**

483. Gustav Stickley Morris chair, #369, sixteen slats under bent arm with thru-tenon construction, replaced canvas foundation, refinished, unsigned, 33"w x 38"d x 39"h, very good condition
6500-8500   March 3, 1996
Sold for $8500

Not Pictured:

484. Gustav Stickley Morris chair, #369, original weathered finish, restoration to one arm, very good condition   5000-7000
August 27, 1995   Sold for $6500

485. Gustav Stickley Morris chair, #333, fixed back, seven slats under each arm, recovered in brown leather, color added to original finish, branded, 29"w x 31"d x 38"h, minor roughness to arm, very good condition   5000-7000
November 24, 1996 Sold for $3750

Not Pictured:

486. Gustav Stickley Morris chair, #333, recovered in brown leather, light recoat over original finish, branded, 29"w x 31"d x 38"h, very good condition   5000-7000   May 4, 1997
Sold for $4250

487. Gustav Stickley armchair, designed by Harvey Ellis, arched seat rails on all four sides, one large slat under each arm, recent finish, box mark, 29"w x 31"d x 40"h, very good condition   3000-4000 May 2, 1993   Sold for $3000

488. Gustav Stickley chair, #390, fixed back with twenty-four spindles under arm, original finish, leather covered cushions, branded mark with original label, 39"h x 29"w, excellent condition 10,000-15,000   March 27, 1988 Sold for $10,000

489. **Gustav Stickley** armchair, #391, even arm spindled cube chair, drop-in seat, recent finish, 26"w x 28"d x 29"h, very good condition   4000-6000 February 14, 1993 Sold for $5500

Not Pictured:

490. **Gustav Stickley** armchair, #391, original finish, large red decal, excellent condition 15,000-18,000 October 4, 1987 Sold for $15,000

491. **Gustav Stickley** armchair, #391, mahogany, recent finish, unsigned, very good condition 4000-6000   February 12, 1995 Sold for $5000

492. **Gustav Stickley** armchair, #391, recovered original spring cushion, original finish, signed with red decal, excellent condition   9000-12,000 November 23, 1997 Sold for $24,000

493. **Gustav Stickley** arm chair, #328, single wide slat to sides and back, replaced cane foundation, recent finish, unsigned, 26"w x 28"d x 28"h, very good condition 3000-4000   February 16, 1997 Sold for $3000

494. Gustav Stickley inlaid armchair, designed by Harvey Ellis, double horizontal rail above three slats, each rail has inlaid design of copper, pewter and wood, replaced cane foundation, recent finish, 24"w x 21"d x 44"h, one small piece of inlay missing, very good condition   6000-7000
November 24, 1996   Sold for $8000

495. Gustav Stickley footstool, #395, with seven spindles to sides with thru-tenon construction, recovered cushion, cleaned original finish, un-signed, 20"w x 16"d x 15"h, very good condition 900-1100   May 15, 1994   Sold for $1800

496. Gustav Stickley armchair, #376, high back with eleven spindles and nine spindles under each arm, recovered loose cushion rests on a canvas sling seat, cleaned and recoated original finish, two spindles replaced, unsigned, 28"w x 23"d x 49"h, very good condition 4500-5500   May 15, 1994
Sold for $4250

Not Pictured:

497. Gustav Stickley armchair, #376, replaced sling seat, unsigned, recent finish, very good condition 3500-4500   August 27, 1995
Sold for $3250

498. Gustav Stickley armchair, #376, in mahogany, reupholstered seat cushion, recent finish, unsigned, very good condition   3000-5000
February 16, 1997   Sold for $2600

499. Gustav Stickley armchair, #376, replaced drop-in rush seat, recent finish, unsigned, 28"w x 23"d x 49"h, very good condition   4500-5000
November 23, 1997   Sold for $4500

To buy, consign or sell these objects call:
(513) 321-6742 or (708) 383-5234

500. Gustav Stickley armchair, #2590, four horizontal slats to back, open arms, replaced rope foundation, original worn cushions, 31"w x 29"d x 39"h, original finish, red decal, excellent condition   2000-2500 August 25, 1996   Sold for $3000

Not Pictured:

501. Gustav Stickley armchair, #2590, original finish, box mark, excellent condition 2000-2500   September 30, 1990 Sold for $1600

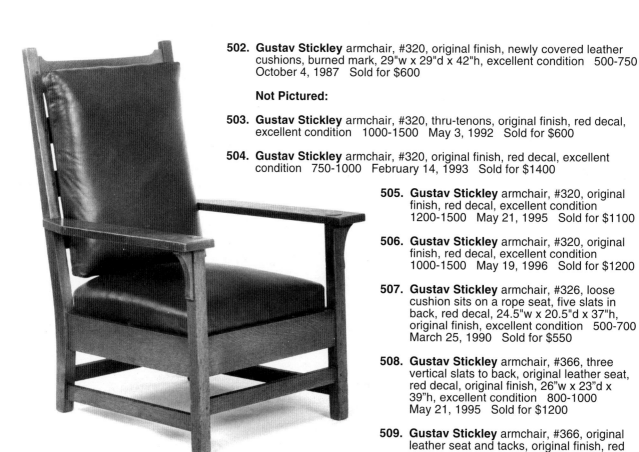

502. Gustav Stickley armchair, #320, original finish, newly covered leather cushions, burned mark, 29"w x 29"d x 42"h, excellent condition   500-750 October 4, 1987   Sold for $600

Not Pictured:

503. Gustav Stickley armchair, #320, thru-tenons, original finish, red decal, excellent condition   1000-1500   May 3, 1992   Sold for $600

504. Gustav Stickley armchair, #320, original finish, red decal, excellent condition   750-1000   February 14, 1993   Sold for $1400

505. Gustav Stickley armchair, #320, original finish, red decal, excellent condition 1200-1500   May 21, 1995   Sold for $1100

506. Gustav Stickley armchair, #320, original finish, red decal, excellent condition 1000-1500   May 19, 1996   Sold for $1200

507. Gustav Stickley armchair, #326, loose cushion sits on a rope seat, five slats in back, red decal, 24.5"w x 20.5"d x 37"h, original finish, excellent condition   500-700 March 25, 1990   Sold for $550

508. Gustav Stickley armchair, #366, three vertical slats to back, original leather seat, red decal, original finish, 26"w x 23"d x 39"h, excellent condition   800-1000 May 21, 1995   Sold for $1200

509. Gustav Stickley armchair, #366, original leather seat and tacks, original finish, red decal and paper label, excellent condition 500-700   May 3, 1992   Sold for $800

510. **Gustav Stickley** armchair, #324, fixed back with five slats under each arm, enhanced original finish, 42"h, seat size 25"d x 22"w, very good condition   1000-1500 May 7, 1989 Sold for $1400

Not Pictured:

511. **Gustav Stickley** armchair, #324, original finish, red decal, excellent condition 900-1200   October 4, 1987   Sold for $900

512. **Gustav Stickley** armchair, #324, original finish, red decal, excellent condition 800-1100   March 27, 1988   Sold for $1000

513. **Gustav Stickley** armchair, #324, red decal, original finish, excellent condition 1000-1500   October 2, 1988 Sold for $1200

514. **Gustav Stickley** armchair, #324, original finish, red box mark, excellent condition 1500-2000   May 21, 1995   Sold for $2700

515. **Gustav Stickley** armchair, #324, replaced cushion in brown leather, recoated original finish, signed with red decal, very good condition   1500-1800   November 23, 1997 Sold for $1600

516. **Gustav Stickley** armchair, #396, original finish, red decal, 32"w x 33"d x 40"h, very good condition 2500-3000 November 15, 1992 Sold for $2600

Not Pictured:

517. **Gustav Stickley** armchair, #396, drop-in spring cushion, original finish, red decal, excellent condition 3000-3500 November 15, 1992 Sold for $3000

518. **Gustav Stickley** armchair, #396, recent finish, branded, very good condition 3000-4000 December 3, 1995 Sold for $2800

To buy, consign or sell these objects call:
(513) 321-6742 or (708) 383-5234

519. Gustav Stickley armchair, #318, five slats to back, recent finish, 27"w x 23"d x 37"h, very good condition 500-700   February 14, 1993 Sold for $500

520. Gustav Stickley footstool, #300, recent finish, 20"w x 16"d x 15"h, very good condition   400-600 February 14, 1993 Sold for $500

521. Gustav Stickley armchair, #316, inverted V-back, thru-tenons, open arms, replaced leather, recent finish, 23"w x 19.5"d x 37"h, very good condition 900-1100   September 30, 1990   Sold for $500

522. Gustav Stickley
armchair, #2603, arched top over three horizontal slats, replaced rope foundation, recoated original finish, unsigned, 27"w x 26"d x 37"h, minor roughness, very good condition
1000-1500
August 25, 1996
Sold for $400

523. Gustav Stickley
chair, #1292, four slats to back under a notched top rail, tapered legs, new rush, original finish, unsigned, 18"w x 16"d x 34"h, minor roughness, very good condition
500-700
August 25, 1996
Sold for $1600

Not Pictured:

524. Gustav Stickley armchair, #2604, four horizontal slats to back with arch to top, thick drop arm, loose cushion, recent finish, unsigned, 25"w x 24"d x 37"h, very good condition 900-1200
February 13, 1994   Sold for $900

525. Gustav Stickley desk chair, #398, short H-back, replaced leather seat, cleaned original finish, branded, 17"w x 15"d x 32"h, very good condition 300-400   May 21, 1995   Sold for $600

526. Gustav Stickley bungalow chair, #1289, hump back and five vertical, tapered slats and a notched seat rail, recovered drop-in leather seat, recent finish, 19"square x 38"h, very good condition 400-600   March 3, 1996   Sold for $800

Not Pictured:

527. Gustav Stickley bungalow chair, #1289, original finish, unsigned, very good condition   300-500
February 12, 1995   Sold for $950

528. Gustav Stickley bungalow chair, #1289, new rush seat, recent finish, unsigned, very good condition 300-400   May 21, 1995   Sold for $950

To buy, consign or sell these objects call:
(513) 321-6742 or (708) 383-5234

529. Gustav Stickley chair, #1291, wide horizontal rail with keyed thru-tenon construction, inset seat recovered in brown leather, recent finish, unsigned, 19"w x 15"d x 38"h, very good condition   400-600 November 24, 1996   Sold for $850

Not Pictured:

530. Gustav Stickley armchairs, pair, variation of the rabbit ear design having a solid seat with keyed-tenon construction at top, recent finish, one signed with early red decal, 23"w x 18"d x 40"h, some restoration, very good condition   1200-1500 August 24, 1997   Sold for $850

531. Gustav Stickley office chair, #362, back and seat of original hard leather, original finish, paper label and red decal, 18"w x 17"d x 34"h, excellent condition   1500-2000 November 14, 1993   Sold for $1700

532. Gustav Stickley chair, #1303, original leather and tacks with original finish, red decal, 19"w x 19"d x 37"h, very good condition   1000-1500
November 14, 1993   Sold for $1000

533. Gustav Stickley rocker, #323, five slats under flat arms, enhanced original finish, branded mark, 29"w x 31"d x 42"h, very good condition
900-1200   May 7, 1989   Sold for $1300

Not Pictured:

534. Gustav Stickley rocker, #323, original finish, very good condition
1000-1500   March 25, 1990   Sold for $2600

535. Gustav Stickley rocker, #323, spring cushion, original finish, red decal, excellent condition   1200-1500   November 17, 1991   Sold for $2400

536. Gustav Stickley rocker, #323, spring cushions, original finish, red decal, excellent condition   1500-2000
May 3, 1992   Sold for $1800

537. Gustav Stickley rocker, #323, original finish, red decal, excellent condition
2000-2500   May 2, 1993   Sold for $2700

538. Gustav Stickley rocker, #323, original finish, branded, excellent condition
1750-2250   November 14, 1993
Sold for $2000

539. Gustav Stickley rocker, #323, replaced cushions, cleaned original finish, very good condition   1500-2000
February 16, 1997   Sold for $1800

540. Gustav Stickley rocker, #323, cushions recovered, original finish, 28"w x 35"d x 40"h, very good condition   2000-3000
August 24, 1997   Sold for $2200

541. Gustav Stickley rocker, #359A, open arms with eleven spindles to back, hard leather seat, original finish, paper label, 26"w x 21"d x 37"h, excellent condition   1200-1700   February 14, 1993 Sold for $1800

542. Gustav Stickley rocker, #373, eleven spindles to back, seven spindles to each lower side, original finish, red decal and paper label, 19"w x 18"d x 42"h, excellent condition   1200-1700 February 14, 1993   Sold for $2500

Not Pictured:

543. Gustav Stickley rocker, #359A, recovered seat, red decal, original finish, small nail holes in top of arm, very good condition   1000-1500   May 2, 1993 Sold for $1600

544. Gustav Stickley rocker, #359, sewing rocker with nine spindles to back, original leather, red decal, original finish, excellent condition   700-900 November 17, 1991 Sold for $750

545. Gustav Stickley chair, #374, mahogany spindled side chair, ten spindles to back, one replaced, seven spindles to each side, loose cushion, sling support replaced with webbing, original finish, red decal, 20"w x 18"d x 46"h, very good condition   2000-3000 November 17, 1991 Sold for $1500

Not Pictured:

546. Gustav Stickley rocker, #359, original finish and leather, red decal, excellent condition   600-800   March 25, 1990 Sold for $750

547. Gustav Stickley rocker, #359, worn original hard leather seat, recoated original finish, remnant of paper label, very good condition   500-700 March 3, 1996   Sold for $325

548. Gustav Stickley chair, #374, sling seat with recovered leather cushion, original finish, red decal, excellent condition   2000-3000   May 21, 1995 Sold for $4250

549. Gustav Stickley chair, #374, leather cushion, original finish, red decal, excellent condition 2000-3000   March 3, 1996   Sold for $3000

550. Gustav Stickley rocker, #2603, four vertical slats to back, open under cut-corner arms, new caned foundation, recent finish, unsigned, 27"w x 26"d x 36"h, chip to back slat, good condition   500-700
May 21, 1995   Sold for $300

Not Pictured:

551. Gustav Stickley rocker, #2603, refinished, unsigned, very good condition   500-700
February 16, 1997   Sold for $450

552. Gustav Stickley rocker, #2603, recoated original finish, replaced rope foundation, signed with red box mark, 27"w x 31"d x 36"h, very good condition   900-1200
August 24, 1997   Sold for $650

553. Gustav Stickley rocker, Thornden chair with two wide slats to back and vertical thru-tenon arms, replaced cane seat, recent finish, unsigned, 21"w x 27"d x 32"h, very good condition   600-800
December 3, 1995   Sold for $325

Not Pictured:

554. Gustav Stickley chair, #1299, Thornden side chair with thru-tenon construction at base, two horizontal slats to back, recovered seat, signed with red box mark, fine original finish, 18"w x 17"d x 35"h, excellent condition 300-500   August 25, 1996
Sold for $850

555. Gustav Stickley rocker, #2637, two wide horizontal boards to back, vertical arms with thru-tenon construction, recent finish, new rush seat, unsigned, 21"w x 19"d x 32"h, scratch to back of top slat, very good condition   600-800
February 16, 1997   Sold for $400

556. Gustav Stickley rocker, #313, H-back, new leather cushion, original finish, 25"w x 18"d x 36"h, red decal, excellent condition   500-750   November 15, 1992   Sold for $600

Not Pictured:

557. Gustav Stickley rocker, #313, original rush seat, original finish, red decal, excellent condition   500-700   September 30, 1990   Sold for $1000

558. Gustav Stickley rocker, #313, slip seat, original finish, red decal, very good condition   400-600   February 14, 1993   Sold for $500

559. Gustav Stickley rocker, #309, three horizontal slats to back, open under arm, original leather and tacks, cleaned original finish, minor roughness to rocker, unsigned, 25"w x 29"d x 32"h, very good condition   600-800   November 24, 1996   Sold for $500

Not Pictured:

560. Gustav Stickley rocker, #309, original leather seat and racks, original finish, decal, excellent condition   600-800   May 15, 1994   Sold for $475

561. Gustav Stickley rocker, #309 1/2, recovered seat, original finish, red decal, 25"w x 21"d x 32"h, very good condition   400-600   October 23, 1994   Sold for $350

562. Gustav Stickley rocker, #309 1/2, three horizontal slats with open arms, lightly cleaned original finish, red decal, excellent condition   500-700   May 15, 1994   Sold for $375

563. Gustav Stickley rocker, #319, replaced cane foundation, original finish, signed with red decal, 29"w x 32"d x 39"h, very good condition   1500-1800   August 24, 1997   Sold for $1600

564. **Gustav Stickley** rocker, #311 1/2, five vertical slats, open arm, original finish, red decal, 26"w x 21"d x 33"h, minor split to one rocker, very good condition   500-700   February 13, 1994 Sold for $550

Not Pictured:

565. **Gustav Stickley** rocker, #311 1/2, recent finish and rush, red decal, very good condition 500-750   April 7, 1991   Sold for $650

566. **Gustav Stickley** rocker, #311 1/2, new rush seat, original finish, red box mark, very good condition   600-800   November 14, 1993 Sold for $900

567. **Gustav Stickley** rocker, #311 1/2, rush seat, original finish, red decal, excellent condition 500-700   May 21, 1995   Sold for $1000

568. **Gustav Stickley** rocker, #311 1/2, original worn leather seat, original finish, red decal, very good condition   500-700   August 27, 1995 Sold for $650

569. **Gustav Stickley** rocker, #311 1/2, mahogany, recovered leather seat, recent finish, unsigned, one rocker repaired, good condition   300-500 August 25, 1996   Sold for $425

570. **Gustav Stickley** rocker, #319, open arms with corbeled front posts, recent finish, new leather cushions, 38"h x 29.5"w, very good condition   1000-1500   September 30, 1990 Sold for $1000

Not Pictured:

571. **Gustav Stickley** rocker, #319, original finish, good condition   750-1000   May 7, 1989 Sold for $850

572. **Gustav Stickley** rocker, #319, original finish, muslin covered seat, very good condition   800-1100   September 30, 1990 Sold for $700

573. Gustav Stickley rocker, #317, five vertical slats, signed red decal, original leather cushion, original finish, 27"w x 23"d x 38"h, excellent condition   900-1200   April 7, 1991   Sold for $2250

Not Pictured:

574. Gustav Stickley rocker, #317, replaced rope foundation with loose cushion, original finish, box mark, very good condition   600-800   October 23, 1994   Sold for $800

575. Gustav Stickley rocker, four vertical slats to back, original drop-in leather cushion on cane construction, original finish, 25"w x 23"d x 39"h, excellent condition   700-900   May 15, 1994   Sold for $850

576. Gustav Stickley rocker, #2625, five vertical slats to back, recovered tacked down seat in leather, original finish, red decal, 27"w x 26"d x 37"h, excellent condition   600-800   March 3, 1996   Sold for $750

577. Gustav Stickley rocker, #365, recovered in old leather, original tacks, cleaned original finish, red decal, 26"w x 20"d x 38"h, in very good condition   500-700   September 30, 1990   Sold for $500

Not Pictured:

578. Gustav Stickley rocker, #365, original hard leather seat and tacks, original finish, branded, excellent condition   600-800   May 3, 1992   Sold for $800

579. Gustav Stickley rocker, #365, original hard leather seat, original finish, branded, very good condition   600-800   May 2, 1993   Sold for $550

580. Gustav Stickley armchairs, #366, pair, three vertical slats to back, open under arm, original leather seat and tacks, original finish, signed with red decal, 26"w x 22"d x 39"h, very good condition   1200-1500   August 24, 1997   Sold for $1400

581. Gustav Stickley rocker, #393, high back with rectangular opening above five vertical slats, corbels on legs, inverted V under arms, original finish, red decal, 27"w x 24"d x 44"h, some wear to finish, very good condition   1500-2000   March 3, 1996   Sold for $2700

Not Pictured:

582. Gustav Stickley rocker, #337, three vertical slats to back, arched seat rails under a recovered drop-in seat, original finish, branded signature, 15"w x 23"d x 34"h, excellent condition   300-500   May 4, 1997   Sold for $500

583. Gustav Stickley sewing rocker, #387, high back has three vertical slats to back and three under seat at sides, worn original fabric on spring cushion, branded signature, cleaned original finish, 20"w x 18"d x 43"h, very good condition   400-600   May 15, 1994   Sold for $650

Not Pictured:

584. Gustav Stickley sewing rocker, #387, original finish, new leather cushion, burned mark, very good condition   700-900   March 25, 1990   Sold for $1000

585. Gustav Stickley sewing rocker, #387, original finish, new leather cushion, burned mark, very good condition   700-900   March 25, 1990   Sold for $1000

586. Gustav Stickley sewing rocker, #387, original leather drop-in spring cushion, original finish, signed with red decal, excellent condition   500-700   August 25, 1996   Sold for $850

587. Gustav Stickley sewing rocker, #303, original rope support and leather cushion, original finish, red decal, 17"w x 16"d x 33"h, excellent condition   300-400   November 17, 1991   Sold for $275

588. Gustav Stickley sewing rocker, #2635, two horizontal slats to back with original rush seat and thru-tenon construction at legs, original finish, signed with red decal, 18"w x 25"d x 31"h, excellent condition   400-600   August 25, 1996   Sold for $800

589. Gustav Stickley sewing rocker, #2635, recovered seat cushion, red box mark, original finish, excellent condition   300-500   August 25, 1996   Sold for $500

131

590. L & JG Stickley Morris chair, #410, seven wide slats under bent arm with thru-tenon construction, recovered cushions, lightly cleaned original finish, remnant of decal, 32"w x 38"d x 38"h, excellent condition
7000-9000   May 19, 1996
Sold for $10,000

Not Pictured:

591. L & JG Stickley Morris chair, #410, recovered cushion in brown leather, recent finish, unsigned, very good condition
5000-7000   February 16, 1997
Sold for $6000

592. L & JG Stickley Morris chair, similar to #410, cleaned original finish, Handcraft decal, minor restoration, very good condition
4000-5000   May 2, 1993
Sold for $4500

593. L & JG Stickley Morris chair, #497, fixed back, five slats under arms with recovered leather cushions, original finish, marked "The Work of...", 32"w x 36"d x 41"h, excellent condition
2500-3500   May 15, 1994
Sold for $4000

Not Pictured:

594. L & JG Stickley Morris chair #498, original finish, Handcraft decal, minor staining to arm, 34"w x 38"d x 40"h, very good condition   2500-3500
May 3, 1992   Sold for $2800
Note: Model #498 is a slightly larger and heavier version of #497.

595. L & JG Stickley Morris chair, #498, original finish, branded "The Work of ...", excellent condition   3000-4000
November 17, 1991   Sold for $4000

596. L & JG Stickley Morris chair, #798, from the Onondaga Shops, five slats under arm, adjustable back, original finish, unsigned, 32"w x 36"d x 39"h, excellent condition   4500-5500
February 16, 1997
Sold for $7500

Not Pictured:

597. L & JG Stickley Morris chair, #798, from the Onondaga Shops, recent finish, unsigned, original caned seat has some breaks, one hole in original leather cushions, very good condition   4000-5000
November 23, 1997
Sold for $4000

598. L & JG Stickley Morris chair #762, arched sides and skirts, arch under arms and corbels front and back, rope seat with recently covered leather cushions, recent finish, 42"h x 43"l x 33.5"w, very good condition
4000-5000   April 7, 1991
Sold for $3600

599. L & JG Stickley Morris chair, #412, paddle arm, open under arms with long corbels, cushion recovered in brown leather, original finish, Handcraft decal, 35"w x 39"d x 39"h, replaced back bar, excellent condition 4500-5500   March 3, 1996 Sold for $7000

Not Pictured:

600. L & JG Stickley Morris chair, #412, replaced back bar, new leather cushions, original finish, Handcraft decal, very good condition 3000-4000   March 24, 1991 Sold for $3250

601. L & JG Stickley Morris chair, #412, replaced back bar, cushions recovered in leather, cleaned original finish, marked "The Work of...", very good condition 3000-4000 November 15, 1992 Sold for $4250

602. L & JG Stickley Morris chair, #470, adjustable back, corbel supports to legs, recovered cushions, original finish, unsigned, 34"w x 37"d x 40"h, excellent condition   1500-2000 February 16, 1997 Sold for $2600

Not Pictured:

603. L & JG Stickley Morris chair, #470, signed "The Work of...", original finish, replaced back bar, very good condition 1500-2000   February 12, 1995 Sold for $3500

604. L & JG Stickley Morris chair, #830, adjustable back, open under arm with corbel supports, original finish, signed "The Work of...", 29"w x 35"d x 41"h, very good condition   1000-1500 May 4, 1997   Sold for $950

605. L & JG Stickley Morris chair, #471, four horizontal slats to back with six vertical slats under arm, drop-in cushion, recent finish, Handcraft decal, replaced adjustable pegs, 32"w x 36"d x 41"h, very good condition   1500-2000
August 27, 1995
Sold for $2600

Not Pictured:

606. L & JG Stickley Morris chair, #471, recent finish, unsigned, very good condition   900-1100
October 4, 1987
Sold for $1100

607. L & JG Stickley Morris chair, #471, six slats to each side, original finish, marked "The Work of...", minor roughness, very good condition
1200-1700   May 3, 1992
Sold for $1500

608. L & JG Stickley armchair, #850, Onondaga shops, fixed back chair with six slats to back and six under arm, original finish, unsigned, 31"w x 30"d x 40"h, excellent condition
1200-1500   August 25, 1996
Sold for $1900

Not Pictured:

609. L & JG Stickley armchair, eight spindles to back, recovered in black leather, original finish, handcraft decal, 18"w x 16"d x 40"h, excellent condition   700-900
March 25, 1990   Sold for $1100

610. L & JG Stickley armchair, #450, six slats to back and six under each arm, finish partially stripped, unsigned, 29"w x 25"d x 40"h, very good condition   700-900   March 3, 1996
Sold for $650

611. L & JG Stickley armchair, #450, original leather on spring cushion, some tears, original finish, marked "The Work of...", excellent condition   700-900   May 3, 1992
Sold for $1200

To buy, consign or sell these objects call:
(513) 321-6742 or (708) 383-5234

612. L & JG Stickley armchair, #814, five slats to back and under seat, recovered leather drop-in cushion, recent finish, unsigned, 27"w x 21"d x 45"h, very good condition   1500-2000   May 19, 1996 Sold for $2100

613. L & JG Stickley armchair, #750, Onondaga Shops, inverted V-back with wide center slat flanked by two narrow slats, arched seat rail, original finish, replaced seat, unsigned, 27"w x 22"d x 39"h, very good condition   600-800 August 27, 1995   Sold for $450

614. L & JG Stickley armchair, original hard leather, partially recoated original finish, unsigned, 24"w x 19"d x 40"h, very good condition   700-900   September 30, 1990   Sold for $475

615. L & JG Stickley armchair, #420, four horizontal slats to back, arched seat rail, reupholstered cushions, cleaned original finish, signed "The Work of...", 31"w x 30"d x 42"h, very good condition   1200-1500   February 16, 1997   Sold for $1100

616. L & JG Stickley chair, #426, four wide slats under each arm and four wide slats to slightly raised back, original finish, signed "The Work of ", 28"w x 30"d x 30"h, very good condition   4500-5500 February 12, 1995 Sold for $5000

617. L & JG Stickley rocker, #401, bent arms with five vertical slats and long corbels under arms, original finish, original leather cushions, "Work of ..." decal, excellent condition   1500-2500 October 2, 1988 Sold for $2550

618. L & JG Stickley rocker, #499, slant arm rocker with five slats under arm, original finish, Handcraft decal, 33"w x 27"d x 40"h, restoration to one arm, good condition 1500-2500 February 13, 1994 Sold for $1500

619. L & JG Stickley rocker, #485, large rocker with six slats under each arm, original finish cleaned, recovered original cushions, unsigned, 32"w x 29"d x 38"h, very good condition 900-1200 February 13, 1994 Sold for $1700

620. L & JG Stickley rocker, #475, stationary back, six slats to each side, corbels front and back, original leather spring cushion, original finish, cushion numbered, 25"w x 23"d x 40"h, very good condition   1500-2000 September 30, 1990 Sold for $1700

Not Pictured:

621. L & JG Stickley rocker, #475, signed "The Work of …", original finish, excellent condition   1500-2000 February 12, 1995 Sold for $3250

622. L & JG Stickley Morris rocker, #831, long corbels under arms, recently covered leather cushions, original finish, red decal, excellent condition   750-1000   March 27, 1988   Sold for $2700

Not Pictured:

623. L & JG Stickley Morris rocker, #831, original leather cushions, original finish, burned mark "The Work of..." on back, excellent condition   1250-1750 March 25, 1990   Sold for $2100

624. L & JG Stickley Morris rocker, #831, original finish, signed "The Work of....", back bar replaced, very good condition   1500-2000 February 12, 1995   Sold for $2100

625. L & JG Stickley Morris rocker, #831, recent finish, remnant of decal, back bar replaced, very good condition   1000-1500 May 21, 1995   Sold for $1500

626. L & JG Stickley Morris rocker, #830, original finish, conjoined label, very good condition 600-800   May 19, 1996 Sold for $1100   **Note: This is a slightly lighter version of #831.**

627. L & JG Stickley Morris rocker, #830, original finish, signed "The Work of...", cushions recovered in leather, excellent condition   1500-2000 May 21, 1995   Sold for $2300

628. L & JG Stickley Morris rocker, #830, original finish, branded, excellent condition   1000-1500 March 24, 1991   Sold for $1200

629. L & JG Stickley rocker, #487, six slats to back, open under arms, drop-in recovered leather seat and back cushion, original finish, Handcraft decal, 28"w x 25"d x 39"h, excellent condition   750-1000   August 27, 1995 Sold for $1200

630. L & JG Stickley rocker, #421, open arm rocker with corbels and arched rails, original finish, marked "The Work of...", 31"w x 29"d x 39"h, excellent condition 900-1200   February 13, 1994 Sold for $1600

Not Pictured:

631. L & JG Stickley sewing rocker, #333, two vertical slats to back, original finish, original leather seat has tear, Handcraft decal, 18"w x 17" x 31"h, excellent condition 250-350   November 14, 1993 Sold for $475

632. L & JG Stickley armchair, #426, bowed arm with four vertical slats, signed "The Work of...", 3/4" height added to back legs, original finish enhanced, very good condition   1000-1500 April 7, 1991 Sold for $900

633. L & JG Stickley rocker, #427, bowed arm with four vertical slats under arm, signed "The Work of...", seat 31"w x 32"d x 39"h, original finish, excellent condition   1750-2250 April 7, 1991 Sold for $2100

Not Pictured:

634. L & JG Stickley rocker, #427, cleaned original finish, signed with Handcraft decal, very good condition   2500-3000   December 3, 1995 Sold for $2900

635. L & JG Stickley rocker, #817, six vertical slats to back, open under arm with corbels, original leather drop-in cushion, original finish, signed "The Work of...", 27"w x 29"d x 36"h, excellent condition 600-800   May 19, 1996 Sold for $1400

Not Pictured:

636. L & JG Stickley rocker, five vertical slats, open under arm, arched seat rail with original drop-in spring cushion, recent finish, branded, restoration to rear leg, 25"w x 20"d x 35"h, good condition 300-400   August 27, 1995   Sold for $350

637. L & JG Stickley rocker, #827, three horizontal slats to back, notched top rail, original leather cushion, branded "The Work of...", original finish, 27"w x 32"d x 32"h, excellent condition 600-800   March 25, 1990
Sold for $750

Not Pictured:

638. L & JG Stickley rocker, #827, drop-in original cushion, cleaned original finish, Handcraft decal, very good condition   400-600   August 25, 1996
Sold for $650

639. L & JG Stickley rocker, similar to #461, seven slats under each arm, light recoat over original finish, Handcraft decal, 31"w x 30"d x 36"h, very good condition 1200-1500   May 2, 1993
Sold for $1600

Not Pictured:

640. L & JG Stickley rocker, attribution, large form having five slats under each arm with an arched seat rail, recovered original spring cushion, original finish, unsigned, 30"w x 36"d x 38"h, excellent condition   1200-1500 August 24, 1997   Sold for $1400

641. L & JG Stickley rocker, #809, five vertical slats under peaked top rail, drop-in spring cushion, unsigned, recent finish, 18"w x 17"d x 34"h, very good condition   200-300   February 13, 1994 Sold for $220

Not Pictured:

642. L & JG Stickley rocker, #809, drop-in cushion, recent finish, unsigned, very good condition 200-300   February 13, 1994   Sold for $190

643. Roycroft Morris chair, #045, large chair with four slats under rounded flat arms, original finish, script signature, 28"w x 23"d x 46"h, excellent condition 2000-3000 November 17. 1991 Sold for $1600

Not Pictured:

644. Roycroft armchair, six slats under each arm, magazine holder under one arm and back, spring cushion, recent finish, orb signature, 36"w x 32"d x 40"h, one corbel missing, magazine holder replaced, very good condition 600-800   December 3, 1995 Sold for $1100

645. Roycroft side chair, #031, heavy high back chair, script signature at top over three slat back, minor restoration, recoated original finish, 19"w x 19"d x 47"h, very good condition   1200-1500
March 24, 1991
Sold for $4500

646. Roycroft side chair, #031, heavy high back chair, script signature at top over three slat back, minor restoration, recoated original finish, 19"w x 19"d x 47"h, very good condition   1200-1500
March 24, 1991
Sold for $3750

647. Roycroft armchair, #028, two horizontal slats to back, original hard leather seat, orb signature, original finish, 25"w x 22"d x 38"h, excellent condition   1500-2000   May 21, 1995
Sold for $2700

648. Roycroft side chair, similar to #027, two horizontal slats to back, wrapped leather seat, original finish, script signature, 17"w x 18"d x 37"h, very good condition 400-600   February 14, 1993   Sold for $400

Not Pictured:

649. Roycroft chair, mahogany, three vertical slats, Mackmurdo feet, drop-in reupholstered leather cushion, recent finish, incised orb, 17"w x 17"d x 38"h, very good condition   300-500   November 14, 1993   Sold for $325

650. Roycroft chair, #030, high back hourglass side chair with original leather seat, original finish, orb incised seat on rail, 17"w x 16.5"d x 43"h, very good condition   500-700 April 7, 1991   Sold for $650

651. Roycroft chair, #030, original leather seat, original finish, orb incised seat on rail, slight damage to top back, very good condition   400-600 April 7, 1991   Sold for $375

Not Pictured:

652. Roycroft chair, #030, orb signature on front rail, original finish, recovered seat, minor distress, very good condition 900-1200   November 24, 1996 Sold for $850

653. Roycroft chair, similar to #029, original hard leather seat, four slats to back, original finish, orb incised on seat rail, 19.5"w x 18.5"d x 41.5"h, excellent condition   600-800   April 7, 1991   Sold for $500

654. Roycroft chair, similar to #029, original hard leather seat, four slats to back, original finish, orb incised on seat rail, excellent condition   600-800 April 7, 1991   Sold for $500

655. Roycroft corner seat, #032, paneled sides with Mackmurdo feet, recovered seat and back cushions in brown leather, original finish, incised orb signature, 21"square x 32"h, excellent condition   3500-4500 March 3, 1996   Sold for $4000

656. Roycroft footstool, #048, tapered legs with replaced leather top, original finish, orb signature, 15"w x 9"d x 10"h, very good condition 500-700   March 3, 1996 Sold for $550

657. Roycroft rocker, five slats to back, thick top rail, inset hard leather seat, wide armrest, original finish, orb incised on seat rail, 24"w x 22"d x 36"h, excellent condition   700-900   April 7, 1991   Sold for $450

658. Charles Stickley Morris chair, four slats under arm, with adjustable back, recovered cushions, color added to original finish, signed, 32"w x 34"d x 39"h, very good condition 1500-2000   February 12, 1995 Sold for $1700

Not Pictured:

659. Charles Stickley Morris chair, adjustable back with four slats under each arm, replaced cushions, refinished, legs slightly shortened, impressed signature, good condition 800-1000   February 16, 1997 Sold for $700

660. **Charles Stickley** armchair, heavily constructed chair with rectilinear cut-outs to back and thru-tenon construction, recovered leather cushion, recent finish, 29"w x 23"d x 36"h, very good condition 750-1000 May 19, 1996 Sold for $1700

Not Pictured:

661. **Charles Stickley** armchair, recent finish, signed with decal, very good condition 800-1100 August 27, 1995 Sold for $1500 **Note: Same form as one shown above.**

662. **Charles Stickley** chair, nine spindles to back, drop-in cushion, original finish, branded, 18"w x 17"d x 36"h, excellent condition 500-700 May 15, 1994 Sold for $450

663. **Charles Stickley** armchair, heavy thru-tenon construction with U-back over three slats, recovered original drop-in spring cushion, recoated original finish, signed, 29"w x 24"d x 35"h, very good condition 900-1200 May 4, 1997 Sold for $750

664. **Charles Stickley** armchair, replaced drop-in cushion, original finish, repair to one leg, very good condition 1200-1500 August 24, 1997 Sold for $1000 **Note: Same form as one pictured.**

665. **Charles Stickley** rocker, replaced drop-in cushion, recent finish, unsigned, 23"w x 29"d x 37"h, small repair to one leg, very good condition 1200-1500 August 24, 1997 Sold for $1000 **Note: Same form as chair pictured but with rockers.**

666. **Charles Stickley** rocker, attribution, armless rocker with three slats to back and worn original leather seat, original finish, 19"w x 19"d x 34"h, very good condition 200-300 February 13, 1994 Sold for $140

Not Pictured:

667. **Charles Stickley** rocker, attribution, heavy chair with three horizontal slats, original finish, old leather upholstery, 28"w x 24"d x 35"h, very good condition 400-500 February 13, 1994 Sold for $290

668. **Charles Stickley** armchairs, attribution, a pair with corbels and slats under arms, slats under flat arms, four vertical slats in back, 28"w x 24"d x 37"h, with cushions, original finish, excellent condition 600-800 September 24, 1989 Sold for $700

669. **Charles Stickley** rockers, attribution, a pair with corbels and slats under arms, three horizontal slats in back, 30"w x 29"d x 34"h, with cushions, original finish, one has roughness to back, very good condition 600-800 September 24, 1989 Sold for $850

Arts & Crafts Furniture
Reference Book

670. **Gustav Stickley** library table, #655, rectangular top with thirteen vertical spindles on each side, original finish, red decal, 36"w x 24"d x 29"h, minor wear to top, very good condition   3000-4000
December 3, 1995   Sold for $3500

Not Pictured:

671. **Gustav Stickley** library table, #655, original finish, signed with paper label and red decal, excellent condition   4500-6500   April 7, 1991
Sold for $6500

672. **Gustav Stickley** library table, #655, original finish to base with cleaned top, paper label and red decal, minor stains and separation to top, very good condition   3500-4500   May 15, 1994
Sold for $3250

673. **Gustav Stickley** library table, #655, recent finish, paper label, very good condition   2500-3500
February 12, 1995   Sold for $3500

674. **Gustav Stickley** library table, #657, mahogany, rectangular top with twelve spindles to each side above lower stretcher with thru-tenon construction, original finish to base, top refinished, red decal, 48"w x 30"d x 29"h, repair to one corner, very good condition   3000-4000   March 3, 1996
Sold for $2700   **Note: Same form as above with thru-tenon stretcher and less spindles in mahogany.**

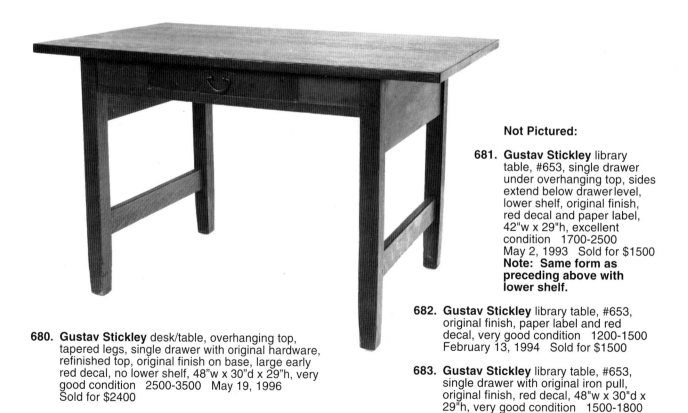

675. Gustav Stickley library table, #652, single drawer under overhanging top, sides extend below drawer, lower shelf, original finish, red decal and paper label, 36"w x 24"d x 29"h, excellent condition   1500-2000 May 15, 1994   Sold for $1700

Not Pictured:

676. Gustav Stickley library table, #652, minor staining to top, original finish, red decal, excellent condition   1000-1500 September 30, 1990 Sold for $900

677. Gustav Stickley library table, #652, copper pulls, original finish, branded, minor distress to top, very good condition 1000-1500   October 23, 1994 Sold for $1700

678. Gustav Stickley library table, #652, original finish, signed with red decal, separation to top, some veneer repair, good condition   900-1200 November 23, 1997   Sold for $900

679. Gustav Stickley library table, #653, original finish, red decal and paper label, 48"w x 30"d x 29"h, some stains to top, very good condition   1500-2000 November 24, 1996 Sold for $2700 **Note: Same form as #652 but wider.**

680. Gustav Stickley desk/table, overhanging top, tapered legs, single drawer with original hardware, refinished top, original finish on base, large early red decal, no lower shelf, 48"w x 30"d x 29"h, very good condition   2500-3500   May 19, 1996 Sold for $2400

Not Pictured:

681. Gustav Stickley library table, #653, single drawer under overhanging top, sides extend below drawer level, lower shelf, original finish, red decal and paper label, 42"w x 29"h, excellent condition   1700-2500 May 2, 1993   Sold for $1500 **Note: Same form as preceding above with lower shelf.**

682. Gustav Stickley library table, #653, original finish, paper label and red decal, very good condition   1200-1500 February 13, 1994   Sold for $1500

683. Gustav Stickley library table, #653, single drawer with original iron pull, original finish, red decal, 48"w x 30"d x 29"h, very good condition   1500-1800 February 16, 1997   Sold for $1400

684. Gustav Stickley library table, #613, recent finish, hammered pulls, top 36"w x 30"h, very good condition   800-1100 October 2, 1988   Sold for $1150

Not Pictured:

685. Gustav Stickley library table, #613, recent finish, good condition 900-1100   November 17, 1991 Sold for $1600

686. Gustav Stickley library table, #614, two drawers with original copper pulls, long corbels and thru-tenon construction, recent finish, red decal, 42"w x 29"d x 30"h, very good condition 1200-1500 February 12, 1995 Sold for $1500

Not Pictured:

687. Gustav Stickley library table, #614, original finish, very good condition 600-800   October 4, 1987 Sold for $990

688. Gustav Stickley library table, #614, original finish, slight warping to top, very good condition   1250-1750 April 7, 1991   Sold for $1000

689. Gustav Stickley library table, #614, original finish, some distress to top, red decal, very good condition   1200-1700 August 27, 1995   Sold for $2700

690. Gustav Stickley library table, #614, original finish, paper label, one chip to drawer, very good condition 2000-2500   August 24, 1997   Sold for $2900

691. Gustav Stickley library table, #615, original finish, large red decal, excellent condition   1500-2000 May 21, 1995   Sold for $2900   **Note: Same form as #614 but wider.**

692. Gustav Stickley library table, #616, original finish, branded, original condition   3500-4500 March 25, 1990   Sold for $4000

693. Gustav Stickley library table, #616, refinished top, original finish on base, branded and paper label, 54"w x 32"d x 30"h, very good condition 1500-2000   September 30, 1990   Sold for $2100 **Note: Same form as #615 but wider.**

694. Gustav Stickley library table, #616, original finish, paper label, very good condition   1200-1500 March 24, 1991   Sold for $1600

695. Gustav Stickley library table, #616, two drawers with original iron oval pulls, corbel legs and thru-tenon construction, original dark finish, branded, 54"w x 32"d x 30"h, excellent condition   2500-3000 February 16, 1997   Sold for $4750

696. Gustav Stickley library table, #616, original finish, signed with red decal, some stains to top, very good condition   2500-3500   November 23, 1997 Sold for $5500

To buy, consign or sell these objects call: *(513) 321-6742 or (708) 383-5234*

697. Gustav Stickley
library table, #460-L, three drawers, early original iron hardware, wide overhang and corbeled legs, original finish, red decal, 66"w x 35"d x 30"h, excellent condition
6000-8000
October 23, 1994
Sold for $15,000

698. Gustav Stickley
library table, #659, three drawers with original iron V-pulls, 13 spindles to each side, lower stretcher, original finish, signed with decal, 54"w x 32"d x 29"h, excellent condition
6500-7500
March 3, 1996
Sold for $8000

Not Pictured:

699. Gustav Stickley library table, #659, recent finish, red decal, roughness to edges, very good condition
4500-5500   May 19, 1996   Sold for $6000

700. Gustav Stickley library table, #659, original finish, signed with decal, excellent condition   5500-6500
May 21, 1995   Sold for $10,000

701. Gustav Stickley library table, original finish, red decal in drawer, excellent condition   5000-7000
February 13, 1994   Sold for $5500

702. Gustav Stickley library table, #659, original copper hardware, original black finish, Craftsman paper label, excellent condition   7000-9000
February 16, 1997   Sold for $8000

703. Gustav Stickley library table, leather top table, two drawers with original copper hardware, flush tenon construction on lower stretcher, original leather and tacks, leather edge strip is missing, unsigned, recoated original finish, 66"w x 36"d x 30"h, very good condition   6000-8000   November 24, 1996   Sold for $5500

704. Gustav Stickley library table, #619, three drawers with original iron oval pulls, leatherette top is old and possibly original, cleaned original finish, impressions in top, red decal, 66"w x 36"d x 30"h, very good condition   4000-6000   May 21, 1995 Sold for $5500

Not Pictured:

705. Gustav Stickley library table, #619, three drawer form with original iron pulls over a wide lower shelf, recent finish, legs re-veneered, unsigned, 66"w x 36"d x 30"h, good condition   2500-3500 November 23, 1997   Sold for $3500

706. Gustav Stickley library table, #619, liming applied to original finish, dark patina on hand wrought pulls and backplates, 66"w x 36"d x 30"h, excellent condition   4000-6000   September 30, 1990 Sold for $2750

Not Pictured:

707. Gustav Stickley library table, #619, some restoration, recent finish, red decal, very good condition 2000-3000   March 24, 1991   Sold for $3000

708. Gustav Stickley library table, #619, recoated original finish, decal, paper label, very good condition   2500-3500   May 2, 1993 Sold for $4500

709. Gustav Stickley library table, similar to #619, three drawers with oval iron pulls, original finish, paper label, 54"w x 32"d x 30"h, some scratches to top, very good condition   2500-3500 November 15, 1992   Sold for $2500

710. Gustav Stickley library table, #3403, trestle form with double-keyed tenons on a slab side which supports lower shelf, recent finish, unsigned, 36"w x 24"d x 28"h, very good condition 2500-3500   May 15, 1994 Sold for $2500

Not Pictured:

711. Gustav Stickley bungalow table, #637, rectangular top with excellent original leather and tacks over a lower shelf supported by double-keyed tenons, refinished base with minor restoration, 40"w x 27"d x 29"h, very good condition   4000-5000 February 16, 1997 Sold for $3250

712. Gustav Stickley library table, #404, elongated vertical keyed tenons into slab sides supporting lower shelf, replaced top, recent finish, unsigned, 48"w x 30"d x 29"h, very good condition 1500-2000 February 12, 1995   Sold for $1200

Not Pictured:

713. Gustav Stickley trestle table, #401, rectangular top over stretcher with double-keyed tenons, recent finish, red decal, 48"w x 30"d x 29"h, very good condition   1500-2000   March 3, 1996 Sold for $2000

714. Gustav Stickley trestle table, #637, original leather top, double-keyed base, some tacks missing, cleaned original finish on base, paper label, 48"w x 30"d x 28.5"h, very good condition   1500-2500 April 7, 1991   Sold for $1500

Not Pictured:

715. Gustav Stickley trestle table, #637, leather top shows wear, original tacks, original finish, red decal, very good condition   1500-2500   March 25, 1990 Sold for $1400

716. Gustav Stickley trestle table, #637, recent finish, unsigned, very good condition   1200-1500 August 24, 1997   Sold for $850

717. Gustav Stickley trestle table #637, recent finish, signed with Craftsman paper label, 48"w x 30"d x 29"h, very good condition   1200-1500 April 7, 1991 Sold for $1400

Not Pictured:

718. Gustav Stickley trestle table, #637, recent finish, some staining, unmarked   600-800 October 4, 1987 Sold for $1200

719. Gustav Stickley trestle table, #637, some distress to top, recent finish, very good condition   900-1200 March 27, 1988 Sold for $800

720. Gustav Stickley trestle table, #637, original finish, branded, very good condition   900-1000 September 30, 1990 Sold for $1500

721. Gustav Stickley trestle table, #637, original finish, red decal, minor stains to top, excellent condition 900-1200   February 14, 1993   Sold for $1300

722. Gustav Stickley trestle table, #637, original finish, black decal, 48"w x 30"d x 30"h, excellent condition 2000-2500   May 4, 1997   Sold for $3750

723. Gustav Stickley trestle table, original finish, unsigned, 60"w x 36"d x 30"h, some separation to top, very good condition   2500-3500 February 16, 1997   Sold for $2100

724. Gustav Stickley trestle table, signed red decal and paper label, top 60" x 36", 29"h, recent finish, very good condition   2500-3500 April 7, 1991 Sold for $3750

725. Gustav Stickley director's table, #632, splayed legs on shoe feet with exposed pegs, originally covered in oil cloth has now been recovered in naugahyde, replaced cleats and restoration to top, 8'w x 4'd x 30"h, good condition   4000-6000 August 27, 1995   Sold for $5000

Not Pictured:

726. Gustav Stickley director's table, #631, important table in original finish with large red decal, 96"w x 48"d x 30"h, excellent condition   17,000-22,000 March 24, 1991   Sold for $14,000

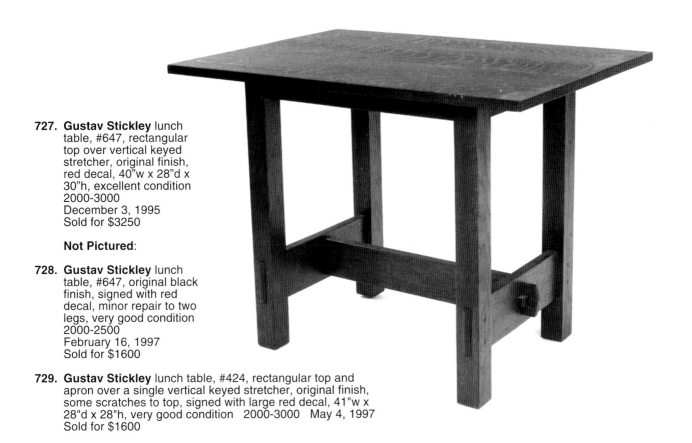

727. Gustav Stickley lunch
table, #647, rectangular
top over vertical keyed
stretcher, original finish,
red decal, 40"w x 28"d x
30"h, excellent condition
2000-3000
December 3, 1995
Sold for $3250

Not Pictured:

728. Gustav Stickley lunch
table, #647, original black
finish, signed with red
decal, minor repair to two
legs, very good condition
2000-2500
February 16, 1997
Sold for $1600

729. Gustav Stickley lunch table, #424, rectangular top and
apron over a single vertical keyed stretcher, original finish,
some scratches to top, signed with large red decal, 41"w x
28"d x 28"h, very good condition   2000-3000   May 4, 1997
Sold for $1600

730. Gustav Stickley
chess table, #419,
replaced leather top
containing dyed chess
board, vertical keyed
tenon support,
cleaned original
finish, unsigned, 39"w
x 27"d x 27"h, very
good condition
3000-4000
March 3, 1996
Sold for $5000

731. Gustav Stickley library table, #650, single drawer with original iron V-pulls and lower shelf, original finish, red decal, 36"w x 24"d x 30"h, very good condition
900-1200   May 15, 1994
Sold for $1100

732. Gustav Stickley library table, #651, double-keyed stretcher, original finish, box mark, 48"w x 30"d x 29"h, excellent condition
1500-2000
November 14, 1993
Sold for $1500

Not Pictured:

733. Gustav Stickley library table, #651, recent finish, paper label, branded, some separation to top, very good condition
1000-1250
October 2, 1988
Sold for $850

734. Gustav Stickley library table, #651, original finish, some staining to top, signed paper label and red decal, very good condition   1250-1750
March 25, 1990 Sold for $1000

735. Gustav Stickley library table, #651, recent finish, red decal, very good condition   1000-1500
May 15, 1994   Sold for $1200

736. Gustav Stickley table, #650, hidden drawer, recent finish, 36"l x 30"h, one drawer, signed red decal, excellent condition   600-800
October 4, 1987   Sold for $550

Not Pictured:

737. Gustav Stickley table, #650, overhanging top, two drawers with V-pulls, tapered legs, recent dark finish, red decal, 48"w x 30"d x 29"h, very good condition 1200-1700   February 14, 1993 Sold for $1300

738. Gustav Stickley table, #650, recent finish, branded and paper label, 36"w x 24"d x 30"h, three repaired holes to top, very good condition   900-1200
May 4, 1997   Sold for $800

739. Gustav Stickley table, single blind drawer above lower stretcher, cleaned original finish, red decal, 30"w x 20"d x 30"h, very good condition   1000-1500
May 19, 1996   Sold for $1100

740. Gustav Stickley drop leaf table, #638, gate leg, cut-corner, refinished, remnants of paper label, 30"h, 40" x 42" top, very good condition   1250-1750   October 2, 1988 Sold for $950

741. Gustav Stickley table, mahogany, narrow drop leaf on straight legs with shoe feet and lower stretcher, refinished, unsigned, replaced hinge, 30"w x 11"d closed, 30"d open x 28"h, very good condition   900-1200
August 27, 1995   Sold for $1300

Not Pictured:

742. Gustav Stickley table, #666, two 9" drop leaves, supported by gateleg, single drawer with original wooden knob, top lightly recoated, original finish to base, paper label and red decal, closed 10"w x 22"d x 24"h, very good condition   2000-2500
December 3, 1995   Sold for $2200

743. L & JG Stickley table, #594, large top over trestle base with wide keyed-tenon construction, fine original finish, signed "The Work of...", 72"w x 45"d x 29"h, excellent condition   7000-9000
October 23, 1994   Sold for $8500

Not Pictured:

744. L & JG Stickley table, #599, large table with keyed-stretcher, cut-out slab sides, original finish, marked "The Work of...", 60"w x 32"d x 30"h, some stains to top, very good condition   2500-3500   May 3, 1992   Sold for $3000

745. L & JG Stickley Onondaga Shops side chair, eight spindles to back, recovered in black leather, original finish, handcraft decal, 17.5"w x 16"d x 39.5"h, excellent condition   700-900   March 25, 1990 Sold for $1100

746. L & JG Stickley Onondaga Shops library table, #1282, c.1907, two drawers with original copper hardware, thirteen spindles to each side, original finish, 42"w x 37"d x 29"h, excellent condition 3000-4000   March 25, 1990   Sold for $3750

747. Charles Stickley chair, nine spindles to back, drop-in cushion, original finish, branded, 18"w x 17"d x 36"h, excellent condition   500-700   May 15, 1994 Sold for $450

748. L & JG Stickley spindled desk, ten spindles to each side, two drawers, original square brass pulls, arched apron, recent finish, unsigned, 36"w x 20"d x 29"h, very good condition   2000-3000 May 15, 1994   Sold for $2600

749. L & JG Stickley desk/table, #565, single drawer with original copper hardware, corbel supports to legs, recent finish, Handcraft decal, 42"w x 28"d x 29"h, chip to top edge, very good condition 1500-2000   August 25, 1996   Sold for $2000

Not Pictured:

750. L & JG Stickley library table, #522, single drawer, hammered copper pulls, corbeled legs with wide stretcher and thru-tenon construction, original finish, Handcraft decal, 42"w x 28"d x 29"h, excellent condition   1200-1500   November 14, 1993 Sold for $1200   **Note: Same form as #565 with lower stretcher.**

751. L & JG Stickley library table, #522, hammered copper pulls, original finish, Handcraft signature, excellent condition   1250-1750   May 7, 1989 Sold for $1300

752. L & JG Stickley library table, #522, two drawers with original copper hardware, corbel supports to legs, original finish, unsigned, 48"w x 30"d x 29"h, very good condition   1200-1500 November 23, 1997   Sold for $1400

753. L & JG Stickley library table, #529, single drawer with original hammered copper pulls, shelf below with double-keyed-tenons, "The Work of ..." label in drawer, 42"w x 28"d x 29"h, recoat over original finish, very good condition   900-1200   April 7, 1991 Sold for $800

754. L & JG Stickley library table, #529, cleaned original finish, excellent condition   900-1100 February 14, 1993   Sold for $1300

755. L & JG Stickley library table, #530, single drawer with original copper pulls, lower stretcher with double-keyed tenon construction, recent finish, signed "The Work of...", 36"w x 24"d x 29"h, very good condition   800-1000   May 21, 1995 Sold for $900

756. L & JG Stickley library table, #531, recent finish, conjoined label, 48"w x 30"d x 29"h, very good condition   1200-1500   March 3, 1996 Sold for $1200   **Note: Same form as #530 but wider.**

757. L & JG Stickley library table, #532, original finish, marked "The Work of...", minor stains to top, very good condition   1500-2000   May 3, 1992 Sold for $1600   **Note: Same form as #531 but wider with two drawers.**

758. L & JG Stickley library table, #532, original finish to base, top refinished, signed "The Work of....", 54"w x 32"d x 29"h, very good condition   2000-2500 August 24, 1997   Sold for $2100

759. L & JG Stickley library table, #521, single drawer with original copper hardware with long corbels and lower shelf, original finish, Handcraft signature, 42"w x 28"d x 29"h, burns to top and overall roughness, good condition   500-700 February 12, 1995   Sold for $700

760. L & JG Stickley library table, #521, original finish, signed "The Work of...", minor wear to top, very good condition   1500-1800   August 25, 1996 Sold for $2000

761. L & JG Stickley library table, #521, original finish, Handcraft decal, 42"w x 28"d x 29"h, minor rings to top, excellent condition   1500-1800 November 23, 1997   Sold for $1700

762. Onondaga Shop library table, #377, single drawer with original brass hardware over a lower shelf with double-keyed tenon construction, recent finish, signed with Onondaga label, 48"w x 30"d x 30"h, very good condition   1200-1500   May 4, 1997 Sold for $1400

763. L & JG Stickley library table, single drawer with hammered copper pulls, wide stretcher with double keyed tenons and corbels, branded, recoated original finish, 42"w x 28"d x 29"h, very good condition   800-1000   October 23, 1994 Sold for $1600

764. L & JG Stickley library table, #1152, Onondaga Shops form in mahogany, two drawers with original brass pulls over wide keyed tenon stretcher, corbeled legs and thru-tenon construction, recent finish, 48"w x 30"d x 29"h, very good condition   1500-2000   May 19, 1996   Sold for $1900

Not Pictured:

765. L & JG Stickley library table, #377, from the Onondaga Shops, thick top over single drawer having original wooden pulls, lower shelf with keyed thru-tenon construction, recent finish, 48"w x 30"d x 29"h, very good condition   900-1200 May 19, 1996   Sold for $2600

766. L & JG Stickley library table, # 377, single drawer with hammered pulls, L & JG paper label inside drawer, original finish, good condition   750-1000 March 25, 1990   Sold for $750

767. L & JG Stickley table, #597, hidden drawer, original finish, 29"h x 28.5"w x 40"l, partial "Onondaga Shops" paper label, excellent condition 750-1000   October 2, 1988 Sold for $1050

165

768. L & JG Stickley table, #599, slab sides with vertical stretcher with keyed tenon, original finish, signed with "The Work of..." label, 48"w x 32"d x 29"h, excellent condition   4000-5000
November 24, 1996   Sold for $5000

Not Pictured:

769. L & JG Stickley table, #599, cleaned original finish, some separation to joints, conjoined decal, very good condition   2500-3500   February 16, 1997   Sold for $1600

770. L & JG Stickley table, #598, recent finish, unsigned, 54"w x 32"d x 29"h, very good condition   2000-3000   October 23, 1994   Sold for $2100

771. L & JG Stickley library table, #511, unusual large form with overhanging top above arched aprons with single blind drawer over lower shelf with thru-tenon construction, original finish to base, color added to top, conjoined label, 72"w x 36"d x 30"h, some staining to top, very good condition   3500-4500   August 25, 1996 Sold for $3750

Not Pictured:

772. L & JG Stickley library table, similar to #511, rectangular top over single blind drawer with arched apron, single stretcher with thru-tenon construction, recent finish, signed "The Work of...", 48"w x 30"d x 29"h, very good condition   1000-1500
November 23, 1997   Sold for $850

773. L & JG Stickley bench, rectangular top over four splayed legs, signed with "The Work of..." tag, recoated original finish on base, top cleaned, 48"w x 15"d x 16"h, very good condition   6000-8000   August 25, 1996   Sold for $4000

774. L & JG Stickley tilt-top table, #589, with original tilt top mechanism, recent finish, branded "The Work of..." , 20"dia. x 24"h, very good condition 900-1200   November 15, 1992   Sold for $1500

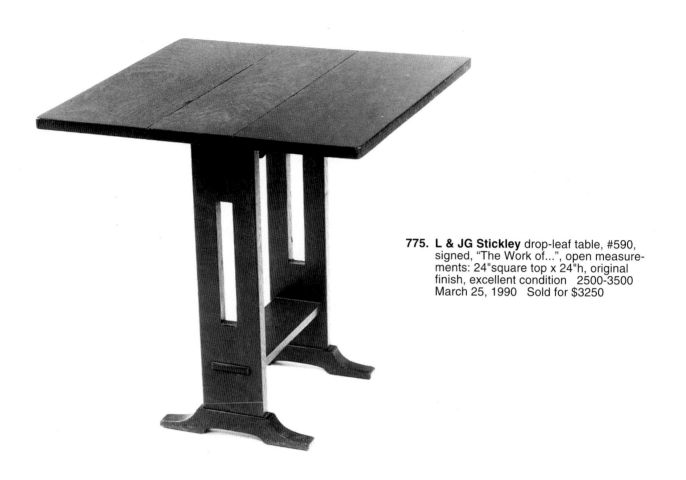

775. L & JG Stickley drop-leaf table, #590, signed, "The Work of...", open measurements: 24"square top x 24"h, original finish, excellent condition   2500-3500 March 25, 1990   Sold for $3250

776. Roycroft Ali baba bench, #046, split log bench, original finish, orb mark, 42.5"l x 10.5"w x 19"h, excellent condition   3000-4000 September 30, 1990   Sold for $5000

Not Pictured:

777. Roycroft Ali baba bench, #046, original finish, original inscription in Arts & Crafts script reads "The Pilars", orb signature, excellent condition   5000-7000   December 3, 1995   Sold for $7500

778. Roycroft library table, similar to #018, rectangular top having two drawers with original copper hardware, five slats at each side all over double keyed-tenon lower shelf with Mackmurdo feet, recent finish, signed with orb, 48"w x 30"d x 30"h, very good condition   3000-4000   August 24, 1997 Sold for $3000

779. Roycroft tabouret, #050 1/2, mahogany, square top with routed edge over four splayed legs, recent finish, carved orb signature, 12"w x 12"d x 19"h, very good condition   700-900   August 24, 1997 Sold for $550

Not Pictured:

780. Roycroft library table, Mackmurdo feet, original dark finish has been enhanced, orb mark, 28"h x 22"d x 30"w, very good condition   700-1000 October 2, 1988   Sold for $1800

781. Roycroft library table, similar to #075 but 48"w, two drawers with hammered copper pulls, top refinished, base original, orb, 48"w x 30"d x 29"h, very good condition   1000-1500   November 17, 1991 Sold for $1300

782. Roycroft serving table, #11, recent finish, signed with orb, 48"w x 24"d x 36"h, excellent condition 1250-1750   October 4, 1987 Sold for $1700

783. **Roycroft** coffee table, Mackmurdo feet joined by cross stretchers below skirted top, 28" square top, 21"h, signed with orb, original finish, excellent condition   4000-6000   September 24, 1989   Sold for $3000

784. **Roycroft** bench, rectangular top over lower shelf with keyed tenon construction, original finish to base, refinished top, orb signature, 42"w x 15"d x 20"h, very good condition   2000-3000   May 21, 1995   Sold for $5500

785. Roycroft library table, #072, rectangular top over lower shelf with double-keyed tenon construction, recent finish, impressed orb signature, 50"w x 32"d x 30"h, some roughness, very good condition 800-1100
February 16, 1997 Sold for $1200

786. Roycroft table, rectangular top over keyed-tenon stretcher, recoated original finish, orb signature, two screw holes filled, 72"w x 42"d x 29"h, very good condition 6000-8000 March 3, 1996 Sold for $6000

Arts & Crafts Furniture
Reference Book

787. Gustav Stickley desk, center drawer and four drawers to either side with wood facetted pulls, chamfered sides with thru-keyed tenons, replaced leather top, original finish with minor restoration, unsigned, 54"w x 30"d x 30"h, very good condition   4000-6000
October 23, 1994   Sold for $4250

788. Gustav Stickley desk, flat top with center drawer and four drawers to each side with facetted wooden pulls, chamfered sides and keyed tenon construction, recent finish, unsigned, 54"w x 30"d x 30"h, very good condition
2000-3000   February 12, 1995   Sold for $4250

Not Pictured:

789. Gustav Stickley desk, #711, flat top with single drawer to center over kneehole opening, pull-out writing surfaces over two drawers to one side, three drawers on other side, original oval iron pulls, replaced naugahyde, one side reveneered, recoated original finish, overall roughness, 60"w x 31"d x 30"h, good condition   750-1000
August 27, 1995   Sold for $1800

790. Gustav Stickley desk, signed red decal, cleaned finish on top, original finish to base, 53"w x 30"d x 29"h, very good condition   3500-4500   March 3, 1996   Sold for $4250

791. Gustav Stickley writing desk, #720, two drawers, iron pulls, three horizontal and four vertical holes for letters flanking two small drawers with wooden pulls, red decal, fine original finish, 38"w x 22"d x 38"h, excellent condition 2000-3000   November 17, 1991 Sold for $3500

Not Pictured:

792. Gustav Stickley writing desk, #720, red decal and paper label, original finish, excellent condition 2000-3000   October 23, 1994 Sold for $3500

793. Gustav Stickley writing desk, #720, recent finish, minor restorations, red decal, very good condition   1500-2000 February 12, 1995   Sold for $2300

794. Gustav Stickley desk, #709, center drawer flanked by two half drawers, paneled sides with flush tenon construction, recent finish, signed with red decal, 42"w x 24"d x 29"h very good condition 1500-2000 August 25, 1996 Sold for $2200

Not Pictured:

795. Gustav Stickley desk, #709, recent finish, small red decal, one pull replaced, very good condition   1000-1500 April 7, 1991 Sold for $850

796. Gustav Stickley desk, #709, recent finish, red decal, very good condition   900-1200 February 14, 1993   Sold for $900

797. Gustav Stickley desk, #709, original iron oval pulls, original finish to base, top recoated, black decal, very good condition   1000-1500   August 27, 1995 Sold for $1100

798. Gustav Stickley desk, #709, recent finish, signed with red decal and Eastwood paper label, 42"w x 24"d x 29"h, very good condition   1500-2000 May 4, 1997   Sold for $1600

799. Gustav Stickley desk, #710, two drawers on each side of center drawer, original hammered copper pulls, original finish to base, top refinished, red decal, 48"w x 29"d x 30"h, very good condition 1500-2000   May 21, 1995   Sold for $1500 **Note: Largest version of form #709.**

800. Gustav Stickley desk, brown leather top with letter rail over two drawers with original hardware above inverted V-apron, cut back lower shelf and keyed tenon construction with chamfered sides, recent finish, unsigned, 34"w x 20"d x 35"h, very good condition
2000-2500   December 3, 1995
Sold for $1700

Not Pictured:

801. Gustav Stickley desk, recovered top in deep green leather original iron hardware, original finish, red decal, 34"w x 20"d x 34"h, excellent condition
2500-3500   August 27, 1995
Sold for $4750 **Note: Same form as one pictured above.**

802. Gustav Stickley desk, #708, desk organizer at back of flat top, two drawers over recessed lower shelf, tapered legs, 30"h x 40"w x 22"d, lightly recoated, large red decal, good condition
900-1100   March 27, 1988
Sold for $1100

Not Pictured:

803. Gustav Stickley desk, #708, partial original finish, red decal, excellent condition   900-1100
October 4, 1987   Sold for $1500

804. Gustav Stickley desk, #453, with desk chair, #2578, flat top desk with letter rack on back, two drawers with original iron handles, original faded green finish, large red decal, 40"w x 22"d x 36"h, low desk chair in original finish, unsigned, 15"square x 29"h, both in excellent condition   2000-2500
May 15, 1994   Sold for $2100

805. Gustav Stickley desk, #708, two drawers with original iron V-pulls and divided gallery at back, paneled sides and back, recently finished, signed red decal, 40"w x 22"d x 36"h, very good condition 1500-2000   August 25, 1996 Sold for $1800 **Note: Same as preceding one with different hardware.**

Not Pictured:

806. Gustav Stickley desk, #708, signed red decal and paper label, original finish, excellent condition 1500-2000   April 7, 1991 Sold for $3100

807. Gustav Stickley desk, #708, original finish, red decal and paper label, excellent condition 2000-2500   February 16, 1997 Sold for $2000

808. Gustav Stickley desk, #518, fall-front with copper strap hardware, chamfered panel sides and back, original interior contains two drawers with facetted pulls and pigeonholes over two open shelves, heavy thru-tenon construction, recent finish, remnant of decal, 26"w x 11"d x 52"h, very good condition   3500-4500   October 23, 1994 Sold for $6500

Not Pictured:

809. Gustav Stickley chalet desk, #505, interior complete including leather writing pad, original finish, red decal, 24"w x 16"d x 46"h, wooden latch replaced, excellent condition   2000-2500 May 4, 1997   Sold for $1800

810. Gustav Stickley chalet desk, #505, mahogany, recent finish, unsigned, very good condition 1500-2000   August 24, 1997   Sold for $1200

811. **Gustav Stickley** chalet desk, #505, paneled door, original wooden lock, pierced carving in arched top, keyed tenon construction, sculpted shoe feet, recent finish, unsigned, 20"w x 10"d x 46"h, very good condition 1500-2000 March 3, 1996 Sold for $1900

812. **Gustav Stickley** chalet chair, #505, single wide horizontal slat to back, pierced cut-out design to back, original rush seat, recent finish, unsigned, 16"w x 15"d x 29"h, very good condition 500-700 March 3, 1996 Sold for $1500

Not Pictured:

813. **Gustav Stickley** chalet desk, #505, recent finish, unsigned, very good condition 2000-2500 December 3, 1995 Sold for $1800

814. **Gustav Stickley** chalet desk, #505, recent finish, restorations, unsigned, very good condition 1500-2000 November 24, 1996 Sold for $1600

815. **Gustav Stickley** chalet desk, recent finish, early red decal, very good condition 1500-1800 February 16, 1997 Sold for $2000

816. **Gustav Stickley** desk, #731, slant front above two half drawers over one full drawer, original oval pulls, original finish to base, branded signature, 32"w x 16"d x 44"h, very good condition 1500-2000 March 3, 1996 Sold for $950

Not Pictured:

817. **Gustav Stickley** desk, #728, fall-front over a single drawer with original iron hardware, all above a lower shelf with thru-tenon construction, interior complete, original finish, unsigned, 30"w x 14"d x 39"h, minor veneer repair to front, very good condition 900-1200 August 24, 1997 Sold for $1000 **Note: Same form as one pictured with only one drawer under fall front.**

818. Gustav Stickley desk, #729, fall front, two drawers with added locks sit atop three long drawers, original finish, paper label and branded, 36.5"w x 15"d x 43"h, three tiny screw holes on one side, very good condition 2000-3000   March 25, 1990   Sold for $2750

Not Pictured:

819. Gustav Stickley desk, #729, drawer locks added later, hammered copper pulls, worn original finish, very good condition   2500-3500 March 27, 1988   Sold for $2200

820. Gustav Stickley desk, #729, iron V-pulls, cleaned original finish, some veneer damage to writing surface, red decal, paper label, very good condition   2000-3000   May 2, 1993 Sold for $2800

821. Gustav Stickley desk, #729, original V-pulls, complete interior, original finish, retailers partial paper label on back, veneer work done to lid, 36"w x 15"d x 45"h, minor stains to top, very good condition   2000-3000 November 23, 1997   Sold for $2700

822. Gustav Stickley desk, chestnut drop-front, keyed thru-tenons, two drawers over one beneath drop front, shelf at bottom, complete interior, original finish, red decal, 38"w x 14"d x 48"h, very good condition   2500-3500 November 17, 1991   Sold for $3500

823. Gustav Stickley desk, #721, slab sides with half moon cut-outs at top, letter rack, drop leaf writing surface, thru-tenon lower shelf, original finish, 38"h, excellent condition   1000-1500
November 17, 1991   Sold for $950

Not Pictured:

824. Gustav Stickley desk, #721, ash, cleaned original finish, branded and paper label, minor chips, very good condition   750-1000
May 21, 1995   Sold for $425

825. L & JG Stickley desk, #662, double door cabinet top with twelve panes, hammered copper hardware, fall-front opens to large writing surface, outfitted with small interior drawers, base has two small drawers over two large with wooden knobs, arched apron, original finish, marked "The Work of...", 42"w x 31"d x 72"h, excellent condition   3000-4000
May 2, 1993   Sold for $4500

826. L & JG Stickley desk, #660, fall-front with two drawers over one, light recoat over original finish, unsigned, 29"w x 17"d x 40"h, very good condition   500-700
March 24, 1991   Sold for $600

Not Pictured:

827. L & JG Stickley desk, #660, original finish, marked "The Work of...", very good condition
600-800   February 14, 1993
Sold for $1000

828. L & JG Stickley desk, #395, Onondaga Shops, ash, slant front, original brass escutcheon, drop front reveals a divided compartment with chamfered back supported by splayed legs on shoe feet, recent finish, some roughness, unsigned, 36"w x 15"d x 48"h, very good condition
1500-2000   May 19, 1996   Sold for $850

Not Pictured:

829. L & JG Stickley desk, #395, Onondaga Shops, recent finish, 33"w x 15"d x 48"h, very good condition   2000-3000   May 4, 1997
Sold for $1700

830. L & JG Stickley desk, #609, two drawers, arched gallery with letter holders at sides, wooden knobs, top refinished, base and gallery original finish, marked "The Work of...", 44"w x 22"d x 37"h, small restoration to corner of top under gallery, very good condition   900-1200   February 14, 1993 Sold for $1300

Not Pictured:

831. L & JG Stickley desk, #500, single drawer over kneehole opening, flanked by two drawers on each side, original copper hardware, tapered legs with thru-tenon construction, original finish, repair to one drawer, some roughness to top, signed "The Work of..", 42"w x 26"d x 29"h, very good condition   800-1000 August 27, 1995   Sold for $650

832. L & JG Stickley desk, #501, flat top, center drawer above kneehole with two drawers on each side, thru-tenon construction, original copper hardware, original finish to base, top refinished, signed "The Work of...", 42"w x 26"d x 29"h, very good condition   700-900 February 12, 1995   Sold for $950

833. L & JG Stickley desk, #503, single drawer flanked by bookshelves on sides with two slats at front and rear, original finish, signed "The Work of...", 44"w x 38"d x 29"h, very good condition 500-700   May 21, 1995   Sold for $550

834. L & JG Stickley desk, #400, one drawer above kneehole opening, flanked by two drawers with original copper pulls, thru-tenon construction, original finish, signed "The Work of..", 42"w x 26"d x 30"h, very good condition 800-1000 February 16, 1997 Sold for $1000

Not Pictured:

835. L & JG Stickley Onondaga Shops partners desk, attribution, original leather top with original brass tacks over single drawer on both sides with original rectangular facetted pulls, flanked by narrow shelves on each side all over a lower shelf with keyed-tenon construction, finish and tacks cleaned, 48"w x 30"d x 30"h, minor roughness, very good condition   2000-3000   August 24, 1997 Sold for $2000

836. L & JG Stickley desk, #512, rectangular top over a single drawer with angled slab sides containing two shelves on each side, recent finish, signed "The Work of...", separation to top, two small drill holes to drawer, 40"w x 26"d x 30"h, very good condition 1000-1500   August 24, 1997   Sold for $1000

837. Roycroft desk, large fall-front over three drawers with iron pulls, paneled sides, three original interior drawers contained in replaced pigeon holes, original finish, script signature, 44"w x 22"d x 48"h, minor distress, overall very good condition   5000-6000   October 23, 1994   Sold for $4000

Not Pictured:

838. Roycroft desk, rectangular top over lower shelf and two drawers having original copper pulls, original finish, orb mark, 48"w x 30"d x 31"h, scratch to top, very good condition   3000-4000   November 23, 1997   Sold for $2000

839. Roycroft desk, large fall-front with iron strap hinges over three long drawers, interior compartment complete, original finish, script across gallery, 43"w x 17"d x 58"h, very good condition   4000-6000   March 24, 1991   Sold for $6500

840. Gustav Stickley Bombay plant stand, #8, hexagonal top and inset Grueby tile on a six-leg base, cut-outs to apron, some color added to finish, unsigned, 18"dia. x 21"h, very good condition 10,000-12,000 November 24, 1996 Sold for $14,000

841. Gustav Stickley-Grueby twelve tile table, exhibits the collaboration between Gustav Stickley and William Grueby, arched apron and a double keyed-tenon stretcher, refinished, unsigned, 24"w x 20"d x 26"h, very good condition 10,000-15,000 November 23, 1997 Sold for $9500

842. Gustav Stickley table, #53T, cut-corner square top with octagonal green Grueby tile to center and flush tenons at corner, notched cross-stretcher with thru-tenon construction, original finish paper label, branded, 17"square x 22"h, excellent condition   8000-10,000
May 21, 1995 Sold for $11,000

843. Gustav Stickley plant stand, #41, splayed legs with keyed lower stretcher, recent finish, box mark, 14"w x 14"d x 28"h, very good condition   1000-1500
March 25, 1990   Sold for $750

Not Pictured:

844. Gustav Stickley plant stand, #41, top has been altered, recent finish, unmarked, very good condition   500-750   March 27, 1988   Sold for $1100

845. Gustav Stickley plant stand, #41, recent finish, early box mark, very good condition   1000-1500
April 7, 1991   Sold for $750

846. Gustav Stickley plant stand, #41, original finish, red decal, excellent condition   1000-1500
November 14, 1993   Sold for $1300

847. Gustav Stickley telephone stand, #605, square top, lower shelf, some stains to top, original finish, branded, 14"w x 14"d x 30"h, very good condition 600-800   May 3, 1992   Sold for $1100

848. Gustav Stickley plant stand, #660, clipped corners and large apron, original finish, red decal and paper label, 18"w x 18"d x 20"h, excellent condition   1200-1500 November 15, 1992   Sold for $1800

Not Pictured:

849. Gustav Stickley plant stand, #660, original finish, branded, minor repairs to one side, very good condition   1000-1500 February 13, 1994   Sold for $1200

850. Gustav Stickley plant stand, #660, original finish, branded, paper label, excellent condition   1000-1500   November 14, 1993 Sold for $2000

851. Gustav Stickley plant stand, #660, recoated original finish, paper label, very good condition   1200-1500 October 23, 1994   Sold for $1500

852. Gustav Stickley plant stand, #660, original finish to base, cleaned original finish to top, branded signature and paper label, 18"w x 18"d x 20"h, very good condition   1200-1700   May 4, 1997 Sold for $2100

853. Gustav Stickley plant stand, #660, cleaned original finish, unsigned, very good condition   1000-1500 August 27, 1995   Sold for $1300

854. Gustav Stickley table, #436, early form, round top with apron over stacked cross stretcher base with nipple, fine dark original finish to base, minor wear to top, box mark, 24"dia. x 28"h, excellent condition 2000-3000   February 12, 1995   Sold for $6000

Not Pictured:

855. Gustav Stickley table, four legs above top with thru-tenons and skirt below, flaring cross-stretchers with nipple, decal under top, old refinish, 24"dia. x 29"h, very good condition   1000-1500
October 23, 1994   Sold for $2500

856. Gustav Stickley tea table, #605, round top over arched cross-stretchers with thru-tenon construction, original finish, red decal, minor separation to top, excellent condition   2500-3500   May 19, 1996
Sold for $1900

Not Pictured:

857. Gustav Stickley table, #607, circular top and apron over round lower shelf supported by arched thru-stretchers, original finish, red decal, 24"dia. x 29"h, excellent condition   2000-3000   May 4, 1997
Sold for $3500

858. Gustav Stickley tea table, #604, light recoat over original finish, red decal mark, 26"h, 20"dia., good condition 600-800 May 7, 1989 Sold for $1000

859. Gustav Stickley tea table, #604, light recoat over original finish, red decal mark, 26"h, 20"dia., minor roughness 500-700 March 7, 1989 Sold for $700

Not Pictured:

860. Gustav Stickley tea table, #604, without thru-tenons, recent finish, paper label, very good condition 750-1000 October 2, 1988 Sold for $750

861. Gustav Stickley tea table, #604, recoated original finish, paper label, very good condition 700-900 May 3, 1992 Sold for $1300

862. Gustav Stickley tea table, #604, cleaned original finish, unsigned, very good condition 900-1200 May 15, 1994 Sold for $850

863. Gustav Stickley tea table, #604, original finish, paper label, red decal, excellent condition 1500-2000 December 3, 1995 Sold for $2300

864. Gustav Stickley tea table, #604, original finish, red decal and paper label, very good condition 1500-2000 November 23, 1997 Sold for $2900

865. Gustav Stickley tabouret, #603, recent finish, 18"dia., very good condition 400-600 September 30, 1990 Sold for $1000
Note: Same form as #604 with smaller top.

866. Gustav Stickley tabouret, #603, recent finish, excellent condition 400-500 October 4, 1987 Sold for $650

867. Gustav Stickley tabouret, #603, recent finish, red decal, very good condition 500-700 November 14, 1993 Sold for $1200

868. Gustav Stickley tabouret, #603, in mahogany, cleaned original finish, red decal, very good condition 500-700 October 23, 1994 Sold for $1100

869. Gustav Stickley tabouret, #603, top recoated, original finish on base, decal, very good condition 700-900 February 12, 1995 Sold for $850

870. Gustav Stickley tabouret, #603, overcoat over original finish, paper label, 18"dia. x 20"h, very good condition 300-400 May 4, 1997 Sold for $650

871. Gustav Stickley tabouret, #602, some distress to top, original finish, red decal, 16"dia., very good condition 400-600 November 17, 1991 Sold for $700 **Note: Same as #603 with smaller top.**

872. Gustav Stickley tabouret, #602, original finish, branded, excellent condition 500-700 November 17, 1991 Sold for $900

873. Gustav Stickley tabouret, #601, original finish, marked with Craftsman label, excellent condition 800-1100 April 7, 1991 Sold for $600
Note: Same form as #602 with smaller top.

874. Gustav Stickley tabouret, #601, original finish, red decal, 14"dia. x 16"h, excellent condition 400-600 October 2, 1988 Sold for $475

875. Gustav Stickley tabouret, #601, original finish, partial paper label, very good condition 400-600 March 24, 1991 Sold for $600

876. Gustav Stickley tabouret, #601, recent finish, unsigned, very good condition 300-400 May 3, 1992 Sold for $550

877. Gustav Stickley tabouret, #601, original finish, water stain to top, red decal, very good condition 700-900 February 12, 1995 Sold for $725

878. Gustav Stickley tabouret, #601, mahogany, recoat over original finish, red decal, very good condition 400-600 August 27, 1995 Sold for $550

879. Gustav Stickley tabouret, #601, recent finish, box mark, very good condition 500-700 December 3, 1995 Sold for $800

880. Gustav Stickley tabouret, #601, original finish, red decal, some wear to top, excellent condition 600-800 May 19, 1996 Sold for $650

881. Gustav Stickley tabouret #601, original finish, red decal, 14"dia. x 16"h, very good condition 600-800 May 4, 1997 Sold for $600

To buy, consign or sell these objects call:
(513) 321-6742 or (708) 383-5234

882. Gustav Stickley tea table, #654, cleaned original finish, 24"dia. x 29"h, very good condition
1000-1500   March 25, 1990   Sold for $1000

Not Pictured:

883. Gustav Stickley tea table, #654, original finish, stains to top, red decal, very good condition
900-1200   September 30, 1990   Sold for $1500

884. Gustav Stickley tea table, #654, original finish, outline of paper label, excellent condition
1500-2000   November 23, 1997   Sold for $2100

885. Gustav Stickley table, #611, cut-corner top over lower shelf supported by cross-stretcher base, cleaned original finish, some stains to top, branded signature, 24"square x 29"h, very good condition
1500-2000   August 27, 1995   Sold for $2000

Not Pictured:

886. Gustav Stickley table, #611, original finish, remnant of paper label, excellent condition
1500-2000   November 17, 1991   Sold for $2500

887. Gustav Stickley table, #611, original finish, red decal and paper label, some minor staining, excellent condition   1500-2000
November 15, 1992   Sold for $1800

888. Gustav Stickley table, #611, recent finish, branded, very good condition   900-1200
February 14, 1993   Sold for $1000

889. Gustav Stickley table, #611, original finish, red decal and paper label, separation to lower shelf, excellent condition   1500-2000   May 15, 1994
Sold for $2600

890. Gustav Stickley table, #611, original finish, branded signature, 24"square, excellent condition
1500-2000   May 21, 1995   Sold for $2300

891. Gustav Stickley table, #611, cleaned original finish, red decal, partial paper label, very good condition   1500-2000   May 19, 1996
Sold for $1800

892. Gustav Stickley table, #611, original finish, paper label, red decal, excellent condition   1500-2000
November 24, 1996   Sold for $3750

893. **L & JG Stickley** table, #577, circular top above round shelf atop cross stretchers, recent finish, small gouge to top, red decal, 36"dia. x 30"h, very good condition 500-750 October 4, 1987 Sold for $700

Not Pictured:

894. **L & JG Stickley** table, #575, round shelf on arched stretchers, original finish, top 24"dia. x 29"h, excellent condition 1000-1500 April 7, 1991 Sold for $1000

895. **L & JG Stickley** table, #575, original finish on base, top recoated, marked, very good condition 900-1100 March 24, 1991 Sold for $1100

896. **L & JG Stickley** table, #573, original finish, Handcraft decal, 18"dia. x 29"h, excellent condition 800-1100 May 2, 1993 Sold for $1500 **Note: Same form as 575 with a smaller top.**

897. **L & JG Stickley** table, #573, recoated original finish, signed "The Work of....", surface stain to top, very good condition 700-900 May 15, 1994 Sold for $1300

898. **L & JG Stickley** table, #573, original finish, Handcraft decal, chip to top edge, very good condition 700-900 March 3, 1996 Sold for $850

899. **L & JG Stickley** table, #573, original finish, signed "The Work of...", excellent condition 1000-1500 August 24, 1997 Sold for $1300

900. **L & JG Stickley** game table, #572, square top with cut corners and an inlaid gameboard over a cross-stretcher base, recent finish, branded signature, 30"w x 30"d x 26"h, legs have been shortened, good condition 900-1200 August 24, 1997 Sold for $950

901. **L & JG Stickley** tea tables, pair, arched stretchers, original finish, late L & JG brand, 20"dia. x 26"h, excellent condition 1200-1600 November 15, 1992 Sold for $2000 **Note: Same form as 573 without bottom shelf.**

902. **L & JG Stickley** table, #543, circular top over a lower shelf supported by thru-tenon cross stretchers, some wear to original finish, branded signature, 36"dia. x 29"h, very good condition 1200-1500 February 16, 1997 Sold for $1200

Not Pictured:

903. **L & JG Stickley** table, round top over round shelf, original finish, unmarked, 36"dia. x 30"h, excellent condition 2000-2500 May 3, 1992 Sold for $2500

904. **L & JG Stickley** table, #536, round top over curved apron with arched cross-stretcher and thru-tenon construction, original finish to base, refinished top, some distress to top, Handcraft decal, 24"dia. x 29"h, very good condition 1000-1500 November 14, 1993 Sold for $1100

905. **L & JG Stickley** table, #536, original finish to base, top has been refinished, signed "The Work of...", 36"dia. x 29"h, very good condition 1000-1500 August 24, 1997 Sold for $950

906. **L & JG Stickley** table, #538, circular top with apron over arched cross-stretchers with thru-tenon construction, recent finish, branded signature, 30"dia. x 29"h, very good condition 900-1200 November 23, 1997 Sold for $1100

907. L & JG Stickley table, #381, circular top with thru-post construction above cross-stretcher base, recent finish, unsigned, 36"dia. x 30"h, very good condition   1500-2000   March 3, 1996
Sold for $900

908. L & JG Stickley half table, a version of #574 with top cut at angle, no mark, original finish, 22"w x 13"d x 30"h, good condition   350-550
March 27, 1988   Sold for $450

909. **L & JG Stickley** drink stand, #22, four splayed legs with cross-stretcher base, thick top above curved apron, original finish on base, top has been lightly recoated, marked "The Work of ...", 18"dia. x 28"h, very good condition   1200-1500
November 14, 1993   Sold for $2000

Not Pictured:

910. **L &JG Stickley** drink stand, #22, round leather top over arched cross-stretchers, original finish, excellent original leather, unsigned, 18"dia. x 29"h, excellent condition   2500-3500   October 23, 1994
Sold for $3250

911. **L &JG Stickley** drink stand, #22, round leather top over arched cross-stretchers, original finish, excellent original leather, unsigned, 18"dia. x 29"h, excellent condition   2500-3500   October 23, 1994
Sold for $3250

Not Pictured:

912. **L & JG Stickley** drink stand, #22, original leather covered circular top, original finish, unsigned, 18"dia. x 28"h, excellent condition   2500-3500
May 4, 1997   Sold for $2600

913. **L & JG Stickley** table, #576, cut-corner side table with a lower square shelf, recent finish, unsigned, 24"square x 29"h, minor distress to top, very good condition   500-700   February 13, 1994
Sold for $650

914. **L & JG Stickley** tabouret, #558, original finish, Handcraft decal, 15"square x 17"h, excellent condition   700-900   October 23, 1994
Sold for $1700

Not Pictured:

915. **L & JG Stickley** table, #576, recent finish, un-marked, excellent condition   400-600
October 4, 1987   Sold for $800

916. **L & JG Stickley** side table, #574, original finish to base, top refinished, remnant of "The Work of.." decal, 18"square x 29"h, very good condition   700-900   August 27, 1995   Sold for $800
Note: same form as #576 but with smaller top.

917. **L & JG Stickley** side table, #574, top refinished, original finish on base, branded mark, good condition   500-700   March 27, 1988   Sold for $700

918. **L & JG Stickley** tabouret, #558, original finish, some stains to top, branded "The Work of...", very good condition   600-800   February 14, 1993
Sold for $1200

919. **L & JG Stickley** tabouret, #558, original finish, Handcraft decal, excellent condition   700-900
October 23, 1994   Sold for $1700

920. **L & JG Stickley** tabouret, #558, original finish, numbered on bottom, unsigned, very good condition   600-800   February 12, 1995   Sold for $850

921. **L & JG Stickley** tabouret, #558, original finish to base, recoated original finish on top, signed "The Work of...", very good condition   700-900
May 21, 1995   Sold for $1500

922. **L & JG Stickley** tabouret, #558, original finish, Handcraft decal, some roughness to top, good condition   500-700   May 21, 1995   Sold for $800

923. **L & JG Stickley** tabouret, #558, recent finish, excellent condition   750-950   March 25, 1990
Sold for $600

924. **L & JG Stickley** tabouret, #558, recent finish, very good condition   500-700   September 30, 1990
Sold for $700

925. **L & JG Stickley** tabouret, #558, original finish, branded, excellent condition   600-900
November 15, 1992   Sold for $1300

926. **L & JG Stickley** tabouret, #559, recent finish, unsigned, 18"dia. x 20"h, very good condition   700-900   February 12, 1995   Sold for $1000
Note: Same form as #558 with larger top.

927. **L & JG Stickley** tabouret, #559, recoated original finish, Handcraft decal, very good condition   600-800   May 21, 1995   Sold for $1000

928. **L & JG Stickley** tabouret, #559, recent finish, excellent condition   800-1100   April 7, 1991
Sold for $1400

929. **L & JG Stickley** tabouret, #559, original finish, Handcraft decal, excellent condition   1000-1500
November 14, 1993   Sold for $1800

930. **L & JG Stickley** tabouret, #559, recent finish, signed" The Work of...," very good condition   900-1200   November 23, 1997   Sold for $1000

931. **L & JG Stickley** drink stand, #587, square top above horizontal stretcher, original finish on base, top lightly cleaned, very good condition   600-800
November 24, 1996   Sold for $750

Not Pictured:

932. **L & JG Stickley** drink stand, #587, recent finish, signed "Work of ...", very good condition   600-800
May 7, 1989   Sold for $700

933. **L & JG Stickley** drink stand, #587, cleaned original finish, numbered, paper label, very good condition   500-700   November 17, 1991   Sold for $700

934. **L & JG Stickley** drink stand, #587, marked with Onondaga Shops decal, recent finish, 28"h, very good condition   600-800   November 14, 1993   Sold for $800

935. **L & JG Stickley** drink stand, #587, original finish on base, worn finish on top, Handcraft decal, very good condition   600-800   May 15, 1994   Sold for $650

936. **L & JG Stickley** drink stand, #587, cleaned original finish to base, top has been refinished, Onondaga decal, 15"square x 28"h, very good condition   600-800
October 23, 1994   Sold for $850

937. **L & JG Stickley** drink stand, #587, refinished top, original finish to base, signed "The Work of...", 16"square x 27"h, very good condition   700-900
May 4, 1997   Sold for $700

938. **L & JG Stickley** drink stand, #587, original finish, Handcraft decal, very good condition   750-1000
August 24, 1997   Sold for $800

939. **L & JG Stickley** plant stand, #24, recent finish, 14"w x 14"d x 28"h, very good condition   400-600
March 25, 1990   Sold for $400

Not Pictured:

940. **L & JG Stickley** plant stand, #24, original finish, signed "The Work of ...", excellent condition   500-700   November 15, 1992   Sold for $900

941. **L & JG Stickley** plant stand, #24, worn original finish, unsigned, very good condition   700-900
March 3, 1996   Sold for $475

942. L & JG Stickley tabouret, #560, worn original finish, signed " The Work of L & JG...", 18"h x 16"w, very good condition   600-800   November 17, 1991 Sold for $700

Not Pictured:

943. L & JG Stickley tabouret, #560, original finish on base, top has been cleaned, 18"h x 16"w, Handcraft decal, very good condition   500-700   May 15, 1994 Sold for $500

944. L & JG Stickley tabouret, #562, recent finish, 20"w x 22"h, very good condition   700-900   March 25, 1990 Sold for $1600   **Note: Same form as #560 with vertical slat under top and larger size.**

945. L & JG Stickley tabouret, cut corner top above an arched thru-tenon cross-stretcher, original finish, signed with Handcraft decal, 16"w x 16"d x 18"h, excellent condition   900-1200   August 24, 1997 Sold for $800

946. L & JG Stickley tabouret, #554, square top over open legs, original finish, branded signature, 15"square x 18"h, excellent condition   500-700   May 19, 1996 Sold for $1000

947. L & JG Stickley pedestal, tallest of this form with square top supported by long corbels on a slightly tapered base with extended feet,
original finish to base, top refinished, unsigned, 14"square x 48"h,
very good condition   5500-7500   August 25, 1996   Sold for $5000
Note: Same form as #27 with larger top and taller.

948. L & JG Stickley pedestal, #27, square top supported by long
corbels on slightly tapered base with four extended feet, recent
finish, unsigned, 12"square x 36"h, very good condition   1500-2000
May 19, 1996   Sold for $1900

Not Pictured:

949. L & JG Stickley pedestal, #28, cleaned original finish, branded, top
13"w x 13"d x 42"h, minor stains to top, excellent condition
2000-3000   March 24, 1991   Sold for $1800   **Note: Same form
as #27 with larger top and taller.**

950. Roycroft tabouret, #049, three vertical slats over keyed tenons, Mackmurdo feet, beautiful original finish to base, top refinished, incised orb, 14"w x 14"d x 20"h, very good condition   1000-1500
November 14, 1993   Sold for $1400

951. Roycroft tabouret, #050, square top, large keyhole cut-outs to sides, recent finish, incised orb, 15"w x 15"d x 21"h, very good condition   700-900
November 14, 1993   Sold for $700

Not Pictured:

952. Roycroft tabouret, #050, original finish, orb mark, very good condition   500-700   May 15, 1994
Sold for $1200

953. Roycroft tabouret, #050 1/2, original finish to base, 12"w x 12"d x 19"h, top with nail holes and wood loss, good condition   100-200   February 14, 1993
Sold for $280

954. Gustav Stickley umbrella stand, #54, four tapered posts with original copper drip pan, light recoat over dark original finish, red decal, 12"dia. x 34"h, very good condition   700-900
May 19, 1996   Sold for $600

Not Pictured:

955. Gustav Stickley umbrella stand, #54, recent finish, paper label on bottom, 29"h, excellent condition   600-800
October 4, 1987   Sold for $660

956. Gustav Stickley umbrella stand, #54, original finish and drip pan, paper label, excellent condition   500-700   May 3, 1992
Sold for $700

957. Gustav Stickley umbrella stand, #54, drip pan missing, original finish, very good condition   400-600
February 14, 1993   Sold for $325

958. Gustav Stickley umbrella stand, #54, drip pan missing, cleaned original finish, signed, very good condition   500-700
February 13, 1994   Sold for $300

959. Gustav Stickley umbrella stand, #54, drip pan missing, cleaned original finish, signed, very good condition   500-700
February 13, 1994   Sold for $300

960. Gustav Stickley umbrella stand, #54, original finish and drip pan, red decal, excellent condition   700-900
October 23, 1994   Sold for $950

961. Gustav Stickley umbrella stand, #54, original drip pan, original finish, red decal, excellent condition   800-1000
May 4, 1997   Sold for $1700

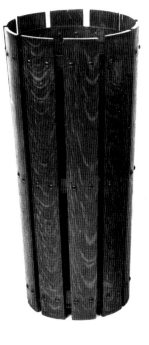

962. Gustav Stickley umbrella stand, #100, iron hoop skeleton, fine original finish, 12"dia. x 24"h, excellent condition   1000-1500   May 3, 1992
Sold for $1500

963. Gustav Stickley wastebasket, #94, original finish, excellent condition   1000-1500   May 3, 1992
Sold for $1500

Not Pictured:

964. Gustav Stickley umbrella stand, #100, original finish, drip pan missing, very good condition
1500-2500   February 13, 1994   Sold for $1700

965. Gustav Stickley umbrella stand, #100, recoated original finish, unsigned, very good condition
1000-1500   May 21, 1995   Sold for $1800

966. Gustav Stickley wastebasket, #94, original finish, excellent condition   1250-1750   March 25, 1990
Sold for $1300

967. Gustav Stickley wastebasket, #94, original finish, excellent condition   1200-1500
September 30, 1990   Sold for $1870

968. Gustav Stickley wastebasket, #94, burned mark, original finish, excellent condition   1500-2000
May 2, 1993   Sold for $1900

969. Gustav Stickley wastebasket, #94, original finish, excellent condition   1500-2000   May 15, 1994
Sold for $2000

197

970. Roycroft table, #073 1/2, recent finish, orb signature, 30" x 30", excellent condition   1000-1500
October 4, 1987   Sold for $1000

Not Pictured:

971. Roycroft table, #073 1/2, original finish, orb signature, 30"dia. x 30"h, excellent condition
3000-3500   May 3, 1992   Sold for $3750

MAGAZINE STANDS, BOOKRACKS, MUSIC STANDS

972. **Gustav Stickley** magazine stand, #72, slight arch under overhanging top, three shelves, fine original finish, branded, 22"w x 13"d x 42"h, excellent condition   2500-3500 May 2, 1993   Sold for $4000   **Note: Same design as preceding one except there are two additional shelves.**

Not Pictured:

973. **Gustav Stickley** magazine stand, #72, three shelves, signed with red decal and original paper label, original finish, excellent condition   1500-2000   March 27, 1988   Sold for $2000

974. **Gustav Stickley** magazine stand, #72, three shelves, recent finish, unsigned, very good condition   1250-1750 November 14, 1993   Sold for $2500

975. **Gustav Stickley** magazine stand, #72, three shelves, original finish, unsigned, burn to rear leg, very good condition 1500-2500   October 23, 1994   Sold for $1800

976. **Gustav Stickley** magazine stand, #72, three shelves, recent finish, unsigned, very good condition   1500-2000 February 12, 1995   Sold for $1800

977. **Gustav Stickley** magazine stand, #514, panelled sides, four shelves with original tacks and leather trim, recent finish, 16"w x 15"d x 45"h, very good condition 1000-1500   September 30, 1990   Sold for $1600

Not Pictured:

978. **Gustav Stickley** magazine stand, #514, original finish, no mark, excellent condition   1000-1500 October 4, 1987   Sold for $1800

To buy, consign or sell these objects call:
(513) 321-6742 or (708) 383-5234

979. Gustav Stickley magazine stand #514, original leather trimmings and tacks, three shelves, original finish, red decal, 15"w x 14"d x 35"h, excellent condition   2000-3000   March 24, 1991 Sold for $3000   **Note: Same form as preceding one but with three shelves.**

980. Gustav Stickley magazine stand, #548, four shelves with paneled sides under a beveled top, minor repairs to bottom, color added to original finish, box mark, 16"w x 16"d x 16"h, very good condition   2500-3500   November 14, 1993 Sold for $3250

Not Pictured:

981. Gustav Stickley magazine stand, #548, recent finish, unsigned, very good condition   2500-3500 February 16, 1997   Sold for $2600

982. Gustav Stickley magazine stand #547, three shelves, partial original finish, red decal, 35"h, 15" top, excellent condition   1500-2000   October 4, 1987   Sold for $1800

Not Pictured:

983. Gustav Stickley magazine stand, #547, cleaned original finish, red box mark, very good condition 1750-2200   November 14, 1993   Sold for $1700

984. Gustav Stickley magazine stand, #547, red box mark, recent finish, separation to one board on top, very good condition   1000-1500   May 15, 1994   Sold for $1200

985. Gustav Stickley magazine stand, #547, original finish, signed with red box mark, 15"w x 15"d x 35"h, excellent condition   4000-5000   August 24, 1997 Sold for $4500

986. Gustav Stickley magazine stand, #79, slab sides with thru-tenon construction, D cut-outs, four shelves over arched toe-board, original finish, paper label, 14"w x 9"d x 40"h, excellent condition   1500-2000 August 27, 1995   Sold for $1700

Not Pictured:

987. Gustav Stickley magazine stand, #79, recoat over original finish, paper label, very good condition 1200-1500   October 23, 1994   Sold for $1700

988. Gustav Stickley bookrack, D cut-outs at top of plank sides, thru-tenons, original finish, red decal, 30"w x 10"d x 38"h, excellent condition 1500-2000 September 30, 1990 Sold for $2600

989. Gustav Stickley bookrack, #74, V-shaped book trough above shelf, keyed-tenon sides with D cut-outs, original finish, branded and paper label, 30"w x 10"d x 31"h, excellent condition 1500-2000 November 14, 1993 Sold for $1500

Not Pictured:

990. Gustav Stickley bookrack, #74, cleaned finish, red decal and paper label, very good condition 1250-1750 May 7, 1989 Sold for $1100

991. Gustav Stickley book trough, D cut-outs to sides, original finish, red decal, 30"w x 10"d x 31"h, excellent condition   1500-2000   October 23, 1994 Sold for $2750

992. Gustav Stickley music stand, #674, spindle sided form with four shelves, four tapered posts extend over top shelf, sides with five spindles, back has seven, cleaned original finish, paper label, 20"w x 14"d x 42"h, very good condition   4000-5000 May 2, 1993   Sold for $2900

Not Pictured:

993. Gustav Stickley music stand, #674, red decal and remnants of paper label, original finish, excellent condition   5000-7000   October 2, 1988 Sold for $7975

994. Gustav Stickley music stand, #670, four shelves with arched gallery supported by tapered legs, original finish, paper label, 22"w x 15"d x 39"h, excellent condition   2000-2500   February 12, 1995 Sold for $2800

995. Gustav Stickley magazine stand, cut-out on side above two slats with three slats to back, four shelves, cleaned original finish, paper label, red decal, 20"w x 15"d x 36"h, very good condition   1200-1700   May 21, 1995 Sold for $1400

Not Pictured:

996. Gustav Stickley telephone stand, #605, square top over lower shelf, distress to top, recoated finish, branded, paper label, 14"square x 30"h, good condition   600-800 May 19, 1996   Sold for $450

997. Gustav Stickley telephone stand, #605, original finish, paper label, branded, minor separation to top, very good condition   900-1200   November 14, 1993   Sold for $700

998. Gustav Stickley telephone stand, #605, original finish, stains on top and small split, excellent condition   400-500 October 4, 1987   Sold for $495

999. Gustav Stickley telephone stand with stool, stand with open shelf under top, recoated original finish, paper label, 21"w x 14"d x 30"h, stool 14"w x 12"d x 17"h, very good condition   1000-1500   October 23, 1994   Sold for $1800

1000. Gustav Stickley magazine stand, three shelves with single wide slat to side, refinished, branded and Marshall Field retailer's tag, 27"w x 12"d x 30"h, very good condition   600-800   October 23, 1994   Sold for $1200

1001. Gustav Stickley magazine stand, three shelves with single slat to sides, cleaned original finish, paper label, red decal, 16"w x 13"d x 31"h, very good condition   700-900   February 12, 1995   Sold for $1100

1002. Gustav Stickley magazine stand, Tree of Life design on canted sides with four shelves, refinished, 13"dia. x 43"h, very good condition   700-900   May 21, 1995   Sold for $900

Not Pictured:

1003. Gustav Stickley magazine stand, Tree of Life design, original finish, excellent condition   600-800   March 27, 1988   Sold for $650

1004. Gustav Stickley magazine stand, Tree of Life design, recent finish, very good condition   500-700   February 14, 1993   Sold for $1200

1005. Gustav Stickley magazine stand, Tree of Life design, replaced leather strip on front, recoated original finish, very good condition   700-900   February 12, 1995   Sold for $1200

1006. Gustav Stickley magazine stand, Tree of Life design, recent finish, some distress to top, unsigned, very good condition   500-700   August 27, 1995   Sold for $800

1007. Gustav Stickley magazine stand, Tree of Life design, original finish, excellent condition   1200-1700   May 19, 1996   Sold for $2200

1008. L & JG Stickley book table, #516, seven slats and bookshelf on all four sides, original finish to base, some stains on lightly cleaned top, signed "The Work of...", 27"square x 29"h, excellent condition   4500-5500   May 15, 1994   Sold for $6500

Not Pictured:

1009. L & JG Stickley book table, #516, original finish, Handcraft decal, minor restoration, very good condition   4500-5500   October 23, 1994   Sold for $9000

1010. L & JG Stickley book table, #516, original finish, red decal, excellent condition   7500-9500   October 2, 1988   Sold for $9000

1011. L & JG Stickley magazine stand, #46, subtle arches at top and bottom support three slats, four shelves, marked "The Work of L & JG Stickley", signed with red decal, recent finish, 21"w x 12"d x 42"h, very good condition   900-1200   April 7, 1991   Sold for $1200

Not Pictured:

1012. L & JG Stickley magazine stand, #46, original finish, branded, excellent condition   1250-1500   May 7, 1989   Sold for $1800

1013. L & JG Stickley magazine stand, #46, original finish, Handcraft decal, excellent condition   1250-1750   September 30, 1990   Sold for $1750

1014. L & JG Stickley magazine stand, #46, cleaned original finish, branded, very good condition   1250-1750   April 7, 1991   Sold for $2250

1015. L & JG Stickley magazine stand, #46, original finish, unsigned, excellent condition   1500-2000   May 19, 1996   Sold for $2000

1016. L & JG Stickley magazine stand, #46, original finish, signed "The Work of...", very good condition   1000-1500   October 23, 1994   Sold for $1900

1017. L & JG Stickley magazine stand, #46, original finish, unsigned, excellent condition   1200-1700   August 27, 1995   Sold for $1700

1018. L & JG Stickley magazine stand, #46, a narrow version, original finish, Handcraft decal and remnant of paper label, 19"w x 12"d x 42"h, excellent condition   1000-1500   November 15, 1992   Sold for $1600

1019. L & JG Stickley magazine stand, #41, rectangular top over two lower shelves with one wide slat to each side over an arched toe-board, original finish, remnant of "The Work of...." label, 36"w x 12"d x 30"h, some distress to top, very good condition   1000-1500   August 24, 1997   Sold for $1600

1020. L & JG Stickley magazine stand #45, four shelves, arches to top, base and sides, original finish, Handcraft decal, 19"w x 12"d x 46"h, very good condition   1500-2000   May 3, 1992   Sold for $1600

Not Pictured:

1021. L & JG Stickley magazine stand, #45, original finish, unsigned, excellent condition   1500-2000
May 15, 1994   Sold for $1800

1022. L & JG Stickley magazine stand, #45, recent finish, unsigned, stains to shelves, good condition   800-1100
March 3, 1996   Sold for $900

1023. L & JG Stickley magazine stand, #45, original finish, remnant of "The Work of..." decal, very good condition
1500-2000   February 16, 1997   Sold for $1800

1024. L & JG Stickley magazine stand, #45, recent finish, unsigned, minor separation to sides, very good condition   1000-1200   November 23, 1997   Sold for $1500

1025. L & JG Stickley magazine stand, #47, four shelves with slab sides and thru-tenon construction, original finish, Handcraft decal, 18"w x 15"d x 42"h, very good condition   1200-1500   May 21, 1995   Sold for $1700

Not Pictured:

1026. L & JG Stickley magazine stand, #47, recent finish, good condition   900-1200   March 27, 1988
Sold for $900

1027. L & JG Stickley magazine stand, #47, original finish, branded "The Work of ...", very good condition
1200-1500   November 17, 1991   Sold for $1300

1028. L & JG Stickley magazine stand, #47, Handcraft decal, original finish, very good condition   1250-1750
November 14, 1993   Sold for $1200

1029. L & JG Stickley magazine stand, #47, cleaned original finish, restoration, Handcraft decal, very good condition
1300-1800   February 12, 1995   Sold for $1300

1030. L & JG Stickley magazine stand, #47, worn original finish, unsigned, stains to top, overall roughness, good condition   900-1200   February 16, 1997
Sold for $750

1031. L & JG Stickley magazine stand, #40, rectangular top over three shelves with arched toe board with single wide slat on side, original finish to base, top replaced, signed "The Work of....", 23.5"w x 13"d x 44"h, very good condition   900-1200   August 27, 1995
Sold for $800

Not Pictured:

1032. L & JG Stickley magazine stand, original finish, signed "The Work of...", excellent condition   1200-1500
February 16, 1997   Sold for $1900

1033. L & JG Stickley magazine stand, original finish, signed "The Work of...", excellent condition   1200-1500
February 16, 1997   Sold for $2600

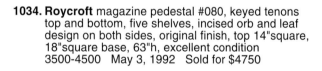

1034. Roycroft magazine pedestal #080, keyed tenons top and bottom, five shelves, incised orb and leaf design on both sides, original finish, top 14"square, 18"square base, 63"h, excellent condition
3500-4500   May 3, 1992   Sold for $4750

Not Pictured:

1035. Roycroft pedestal, in mahogany, thick top above four shelves supported by splayed slab sides with double-keyed tenon supports at top and bottom, original finish, incised orb on each side, 29"w x 18"d x 50"h, very good condition   4500-5500
May 4, 1997   Sold for $4750

1036. Roycroft pedestal, #080, mahogany with keyed tenons top and bottom, original finish with some restoration, incised orb, 22"w x 16"d x 50"h, very good condition 2500-3500   November 14, 1993   Sold for $4000

1037. Roycroft magazine stand, #079, notched top with five shelves and slightly flared slab sides, script signature, original finish, minor stains to shelves, 18"w x 16"d x 50"h, very good condition   2000-3000   August 27, 1995 Sold for $3750

1038. Roycroft magazine rack #78, three shelves with arched sides and back, orb signature, original finish with recoat, 37"h x 16"d x 18"w, excellent condition 2000-3000 April 7, 1991 Sold for $2000

Not Pictured:

1039. Roycroft magazine rack, #78, recent finish, orb mark, very good condition 1000-1500 February 14, 1993 Sold for $1600

1040. Roycroft bookshelf, #087 1/2, three shelves with slatted side and back, original finish, orb signature, 32"w x 16"d x 39"h, three small tack holes under top, excellent condition 4500-5500 December 3, 1995 Sold for $8500

1041. L & JG Stickley footstool, #1292, seven spindles to sides, replaced leather seat, arched seat rail, original finish, unsigned, 18"w x 13"d x 16"h, minor roughness, very good condition 600-800 November 24, 1996 Sold for $700

1042. Gustav Stickley footstool, #729, leather seat with arched rail and thru-tenon construction, replaced leather, recent finish, 20"w x 16"d x 16"h, very good condition 700-900 November 24, 1996 Sold for $900

Not Pictured:

1043. L & JG Stickley footstool, #1292, seven spindles per side, arched cross rail, replaced leather, recent finish, Handcraft decal, very good condition 700-900 November 14, 1993 Sold for $1300

1044. Gustav Stickley footstool, #729, new leather seat, cleaned original finish, very good condition 500-750 November 15, 1992 Sold for $900

1045. Gustav Stickley footstool, #299, old replaced leather, original finish, burned mark, 16"w x 9"h, excellent condition 600-800 March 25, 1990 Sold for $650

1046. Gustav Stickley footstool, #299, original leather and tacks with a cleaned original finish, red decal, excellent condition 900-1200 September 30, 1990 Sold for $600

1047. L & JG Stickley footstool, #391, original hard leather and finish, marked "The Work of...", 19"w x 14"d x 18"h, excellent condition 400-600 May 3, 1992 Sold for $500

1048. L & JG Stickley footstool, #391, recent finish, new leather, very good condition 250-350 March 27, 1988 Sold for $475

1049. L & JG Stickley footstool, #391, original leather seat, recent finish, unsigned, very good condition 300-400 November 14, 1993 Sold for $400

1050. L & JG Stickley footstool, #394, leather top, red mark on leg, original finish, 16"h x 19"w x 15"d, excellent condition 600-900 April 7, 1991 Sold for $700

1051. L & JG Stickley footstool, #394, original leather and tacks, leather is torn, original finish, unsigned, very good condition 500-700 February 13, 1994 Sold for $375

1052. L & JG Stickley footstool, #394, original leatherette and tacks, original finish, signed "The Work of...", excellent condition 400-600 October 23, 1994 Sold for $900

1053. L &JG Stickley footstool, #394, mahogany, replaced leather cover, original finish, remnant of paper label, very good condition 400-600 February 12, 1995 Sold for $650

1054. L & JG Stickley footstool, #394, upholstered seat, recent finish, unsigned, very good condition 300-400 February 12, 1995 Sold for $350

1055. L & JG Stickley footstool, #397, drop-in spring cushion, original finish, branded "The Work of...", 20"w x 14"d x 16"h, excellent condition 300-500 May 21, 1995 Sold for $400

1056. L & JG Stickley footstool, #399, attribution, collapsible stool, series of S-shaped slats pivoting at center, original finish, unsigned, 16"w x 16"d x 17"h, very good condition 400-600 February 12, 1995 Sold for $1200

1057. Gustav Stickley footstool, #395, seven spindles to each side and thru-tenon construction, recovered hard leather seat, recent finish, unsigned, 20"w x 16"d x 15"h, very good condition 2000-2500 May 4, 1997 Sold for $3250

1058. Gustav Stickley footstool, #302, original finish, new hard leather, branded, 12"w x 12"d x 15"h, excellent condition   500-700   May 3, 1992   Sold for $675

Not Pictured:

1059. Gustav Stickley footstool, #302, original leather is split, red decal, original finish   700-900   March 27, 1988   Sold for $650

1060. Gustav Stickley footstool, #302, original finish, red decal, original leather, excellent condition   600-800   October 2, 1988   Sold for $700

1061. Gustav Stickley footstool, #302, with original leather, tears to leather, original finish, unsigned, outline of paper label, very good condition   600-800   August 25, 1996   Sold for $400

1062. Gustav Stickley footstool, #300, fine original finish, covered in new hard leather with original tacks, red decal, 21"w x 17"d x 15"h, excellent condition   700-1000   May 3, 1992   Sold for $900

Not Pictured:

1063. Gustav Stickley footstool, #300, original finish, recovered seat, branded, very good condition   500-700   May 15, 1994   Sold for $650

1064. Gustav Stickley footstool, #300, red decal, Eastwood paper label, original finish, excellent condition   1000-1500   May 21, 1995   Sold for $2200

1065. Gustav Stickley footstool, #300, original finish, new leather with original tacks, red decal, excellent condition   700-1000   May 3, 1992   Sold for $900

1066. Gustav Stickley footstool, #300, recent finish, very good condition   400-600   February 14, 1993   Sold for $500

1067. Gustav Stickley footstool, #300, original light finish, replaced leather with original tacks, red decal and paper label, excellent condition   750-1000   November 14, 1993   Sold for $1100

1068. Gustav Stickley footstool, #300, cleaned original finish, replaced leather, signed with red decal, very good condition   700-900   May 4, 1997   Sold for $950

1069. Gustav Stickley footstool, #300, recovered, cleaned original finish, unsigned, very good condition   700-900   November 23, 1997   Sold for $1200

1070. Gustav Stickley footstool #301, c.1907, mahogany footrest, with new rush, 20"w x 16"d x 18"h, refinished, very good condition   200-300   May 3, 1992   Sold for $150

1071. Gustav Stickley footstool, #301, replaced rush seat with tapered legs, recent finish, very good condition   400-600   February 12, 1995   Sold for $300

1072. Gustav Stickley footstool, #301, replaced rush seat, original finish, red decal, very good condition   300-500   March 3, 1996   Sold for $400

1073. Roycroft footstool, rectangular form with incised orb signature, original finish, recovered drop-in cushion, 17"w x 12"d x 14"h, minor roughness to edges, very good condition
800-1100   November 24, 1996   Sold for $1200

Not Pictured:

1074. Roycroft footstool, drop-in original leather cushion, original dark finish, orb mark, 17"w x 12"d x 14"h, leather is torn, very good condition
500-700   May 15, 1994   Sold for $600

1075. Roycroft footstool, #048, tapered legs with reupholstered cushion, original finish, orb mark, 15"w x 9"d x 10"h, very good condition
300-500   October 23, 1994   Sold for $550

1076. Roycroft footstool, ash, Mackmurdo feet, drop-in rope foundation, missing loose cushion, original finish, unsigned, 25"w x 22"d x 12"h, very good condition   300-500
December 3, 1995   Sold for $350

1077. Gustav Stickley costumer, #53, four extra hooks on double tapered pole construction on a shoe foot base, original finish, red decal, 13"w x 72"h, excellent condition
2500-3500   May 19, 1996   Sold for $3250

1078. Gustav Stickley costumer, #53, tapered posts supported by shoe feet, original copper hooks, light recoat over original finish, red decal, 13"w x 23"d x 71"h, very good condition   1750-2000   December 3, 1995   Sold for $1900
Note: Same form as preceding one with normal amount of hooks.

Not Pictured:

1079. Gustav Stickley costumer, #53, original hooks, recent finish, branded, very good condition   1000-1500   February 14, 1993   Sold for $1300

1080. Gustav Stickley costumer, #53, burned mark on foot, recoat over original finish, very good condition   1500-2000   February 13, 1994   Sold for $1900

1081. Gustav Stickley costumer, #53, original iron hooks, original finish, red decal, hooks have been off, very good condition   1200-1500   August 27, 1995   Sold for $1100

1082. Gustav Stickley costumer, #53, original hooks, original finish, branded signature, 13"w x 22"d x 72"h, excellent condition   2000-3000   August 24, 1997   Sold for $1900

1083. Gustav Stickley costumer, #52, single pole with four original iron hooks, recent finish, unsigned, 27"dia. x 72"h, very good condition 700-900   October 23, 1994   Sold for $550

Not Pictured:

1084. Gustav Stickley costumer, #52, repaired base, recent finish, branded, good condition   600-800   May 2, 1993   Sold for $750

1085. Gustav Stickley costumer, #52, worn original finish, some separation to base, unsigned, very good condition   700-900 May 4, 1997   Sold for $600

1086. Gustav Stickley costumer, single pole with original iron hooks, unsigned, original finish, 23"dia. x 72"h, very good condition 700-900   August 25, 1996   Sold for $500

1087. L & JG Stickley costumer, wide double pole form with six original brass hooks, corbel supports on shoe feet, signed "The Work of..", original finish, 32"w x 72"h, very good condition   2000-2500   May 19, 1996   Sold for $1900

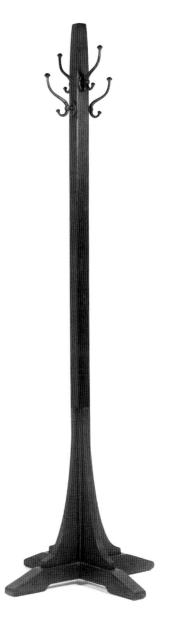

1088. L & JG Stickley costumer, #89, single pole with corbeled cruciform base, original finish, Handcraft decal, 25"dia. x 72"h, excellent condition 700-900   May 21, 1995   Sold for $750

Not Pictured:

1089. L & JG Stickley costumer, #89, original iron hooks, original finish, unsigned, excellent condition   1000-1500   May 15, 1994   Sold for $1300

1090. L & JG Stickley costumer, #89, original hooks, recent finish, unsigned, excellent condition   800-1000   February 12, 1995   Sold for $900

1091. L & JG Stickley costumer, #89, original hooks, original finish, signed "The Work of...", excellent condition   700-900   March 3, 1996   Sold for $650

Arts & Crafts Furniture
Reference Book

1092. Gustav Stickley child's dresser, #921, two small drawers over two large drawers with original copper pulls, original mirror flanked by three-slat gallery on each side, original finish, red decal, 36"w x 16"d x 52"h, excellent condition   3000-4000
December 3, 1995   Sold for $3000

1093. Gustav Stickley child's table, #658, circular top ever cross-stretcher base, original finish, red decal, 24"dia. x 20"h, minor wear to top   900-1200
December 3, 1995   Sold for $1000

1094. Gustav Stickley child's settle, #215, in maple, two horizontal slats to back with sculpted slab sides, lower stretcher supported by keyed tenon and thru-tenons to back, original finish, red decal, 42"w x 14"d x 30"h, minor chips to front edge, very good condition   2000-2500   December 3, 1995
Sold for $3250

Not Pictured:

1095. Gustav Stickley child's table, #658, original finish, red decal and paper label, minor separation to top, very good condition   700-900   May 15, 1994
Sold for $850

1096. Gustav Stickley child's settle, #215, cleaned finish, red decal, replaced key with repair to one tenon and a chip to seat, very good condition   700-900   May 15, 1994   Sold for $950

1097. Gustav Stickley child's table, #658, cleaned original finish, partial paper label and red decal, 24"dia. x 20"h, height possibly altered, very good condition   600-800   August 24, 1997
Sold for $750

To buy, consign or sell these objects call:
(513) 321-6742 or (708) 383-5234

1098. Gustav Stickley child's chair, #344, three horizontal slats to back, recent finish, unmarked, 26"h, very good condition   300-500   March 3, 1996 Sold for $550

1099. Gustav Stickley child's table, #640, thru-tenon construction under rectangular top, recent finish, red decal, 28"w x 18"h, very good condition 600-800   March 3, 1996   Sold for $1200

1100. Gustav Stickley child's chair, #344, recent finish, 26"h, unmarked, very good condition   300-500 March 3, 1996   Sold for $550

Not Pictured:

1101. Gustav Stickley child's chair, #344, seat is missing, recent finish, branded, very good condition 300-500   October 23, 1994   Sold for $400

1102. Gustav Stickley child's rocker, #343, three horizontal slats to back, cleaned original finish, red decal, 18"w x 14"d x 25"h, very good condition 300-500   October 23, 1994   Sold for $475

1103. Gustav Stickley child's rocker, #343, original hard leather seat, original finish, red decal, paper label, excellent condition   600-800   May 21, 1995 Sold for $850

1104. Gustav Stickley child's rocker, #343, recovered seat, original finish, red decal, excellent condition 500-700   February 13, 1994   Sold for $750

1105. Gustav Stickley child's rocker, #343, recoated original finish, very good condition   300-500 May 3, 1992   Sold for $400

1106. Gustav Stickley child's set, two chairs, #342 and table, #658, table in original finish, 20"h x 23.5" top, top warped, one chair has red cushion, other brown leather, only one chair marked with burn mark on back stretcher, original finish, 23.5"h, 13"d, chairs need some work, good condition   450-650   March 27, 1988 Sold for $1300

Not Pictured:

1107. Gustav Stickley child's chair, #342, two horizontal slats to back with original leather seat, original finish, red decal, excellent condition   400-600   May 15, 1994   Sold for $450

1108. Gustav Stickley child's chair, #342, two horizontal slats to back, replaced leather seat, recent finish, unsigned, 24"h, good condition 300-500   February 12, 1995   Sold for $400

1109. Gustav Stickley smoker's cabinet, c.1904, very unusual form having a flip-top which opens to a larger surface above a single drawer and panel door over an arched toe-board, original iron hardware, original finish, small chip in top, signed with red decal, 20"w x 16"d x 30"h, excellent condition 5000-7000   November 24, 1996   Sold for $11,000

Not Pictured:

1110. L & JG Stickley smoker's cabinet, #26, rectangular overhanging top with single drawer and paneled door with divided compartment, original hammered copper hardware and original key lock, original finish, unsigned, 20"w x 15"d x 29"h, excellent condition 3000-3500   March 3, 1996   Sold for $3250

1111. L & JG Stickley smoker's cabinet, #26, rectangular over hanging top over single drawer with paneled door, and divided compartment, original hardware has been polished, recent finish, red decal, very good condition   2000-2500   November 24, 1996   Sold for $2300

1112. Gustav Stickley cellarette, #86, flip-top lid with exposed dovetail construction, opens to a two-tiered copper lined shelf over a single drawer and single door cabinet, interior contains a smaller locking cabinet and open shelves, revolving bottle rack is missing, recent finish new veneer on door, red decal, 24"w x 18"d x 43"h, very good condition   2000-3000 May 21, 1995   Sold for $2400

Not Pictured:

1113. Gustav Stickley cellarette, #86, recent finish with restorations, very good condition   2000-3000 October 2, 1988   Sold for $1950

1114. Gustav Stickley somno, #605, flat top above V-shaped apron, lower compartment with V-board sides behind paneled door, thru-tenons above and below door with wooden facetted knob, original finish, 18"w x 16"d x 30"h, excellent condition 6500-8500   November 15, 1992   Sold for $7000

1115. Gustav Stickley smoker's cabinet, #89, hammered iron strap hardware on cabinet door, small drawer with V-pull above cabinet, arched apron and sides, original finish, red decal, 20"w x 14"d x 29"h, some marks to top, excellent condition   6000-8000 May 2, 1993   Sold for $9500

Not Pictured:

1116. Gustav Stickley smoker's cabinet, #89, single door over arched apron with thru-tenon construction, original finish, red decal and paper label, 20"w x 15"d x 29"h, excellent condition   2500-3500 May 15, 1994   Sold for $3750 **Note: Same form as one pictured above without the hardware and having wooden pulls.**

1117. Gustav Stickley smoker's cabinet, #89, recent finish, paper label, very good condition   2500-3500 November 14, 1993   Sold for $1600

1118. Gustav Stickley somno, #522, early example, c.1902, chamfered and thru-tenons on all four sides, small interior drawer, original finish, top touched up, red decal, 17"w x 15"d x 27"h, very good condition   2500-3500   February 13, 1994   Sold for $5000

Not Pictured:

1119. Gustav Stickley somno, #522, color added to original finish, red decal, slight roughness to top, minute restoration, 17"w x 15"d x 27"h, very good condition   4000-6000   November 24, 1996   Sold for $5000

1120. L & JG Stickley smoker's cabinet, #26, rectangular overhanging top with single drawer and paneled door with divided compartment, original hammered copper hardware and original key lock, top refinished, original finish on base, Handcraft signature, 20"w x 15"d x 29"h, very good condition   3000-3500   December 3, 1995   Sold for $3500

Not Pictured:

1121. L & JG Stickley smoker's cabinet, #26, color added to original finish, sanding marks to top, Handcraft decal, very good condition   1500-2000   November 14, 1993   Sold for $1900

1122. L & JG Stickley smoker's cabinet, #26, recoat over original finish, Handcraft decal, minor stains to top, very good condition   2500-3500   May 21, 1995   Sold for $3500

1123. L & JG Stickley smoker's cabinet, #26, original finish, unsigned, excellent condition   3000-3500   March 3, 1996   Sold for $3250

1124. L & JG Stickley smokers cabinet, #26, original finish, signed Handcraft decal, excellent condition   3000-4000   May 4, 1997   Sold for $3250

1125. Gustav Stickley liquor cabinet, paneled drop-front above a single drawer over two cabinet doors, thru-tenon construction and an arched toe-board, interior contains hand-hammered copper serving trays, red decal, small repair to lid, original finish, 26"w x 14"w x 52"h, excellent condition   10,000-15,000
November 24, 1996   Sold for $13,000

1126. Gustav Stickley book cabinet, #93, original finish, Eastwood label, 17"w x 11"d x 40"h, excellent condition
3000-4000   March 25, 1990   Sold for $2500

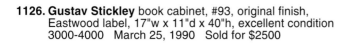

1127. Gustav Stickley music cabinet, #70, single paneled door with original iron hardware, thru-tenon construction on slab sides, original finish, paper label, 20"w x 16"d x 46"h, excellent condition   3500-4500   October 23, 1994 Sold for $5000

1128. Gustav Stickley music cabinet, #70, has a single door with ten sections of four square leaded panes, original copper V-pulls, slab sides with thru-tenon construction, three original adjustable shelves, lightly cleaned original finish, paper label and red decal, 20"w x 16"d x 46"h, excellent condition   5500-7500   May 21, 1995 Sold for $9500   **Note: Same form as preceding one with leaded glass door.**

1129. Gustav Stickley
bridal chest, cedar-lined piece with paneled sides and arched corbels, original patina on the copper corner brackets and hinges, original finish, signed with red box mark, 41"w x 21"d x 25"h, excellent condition 8000-11,000
May 15, 1994
Sold for $12,000

1130. Gustav Stickley bridal chest, double iron hardware and paneled sides with arched corbels, cedar lined, recent finish, unsigned, 41"w x 21"d x 24"h, legs have been slightly shortened, very good condition   4500-5500
October 23, 1994   Sold for $6500

1131. Gustav Stickley shirt-waist box, thru-tenons at top and bottom, excellent original finish, paper label, 16"h x 30"w x 16"d, excellent condition 3000-5000 March 27, 1988 Sold for $4500

Not Pictured:

1132. Gustav Stickley shirtwaist box, #95, eleven spindles to each side, recessed paneled top, recent finish, paper label, 30"w x 16"d x 16"h, very good condition 2500-3500 November 15, 1992 Sold for $4000

1133. Gustav Stickley shirtwaist box, #95, recent finish, crack to top, chips on edge, unsigned, very good condition 4000-5000 May 19, 1996 Sold for $3750

1134. Gustav Stickley shirtwaist box, #95, original finish, signed with paper label, loose veneer on front and back panels, very good condition 7000-9000 May 4, 1997 Sold for $7000

1135. Gustav Stickley wash-stand, two half-drawers over two cabinet doors with square copper strap hinges, all with original oval copper hardware over arched toe-board, paneled sides with thru-tenon construction, original finish, some separation and stains to top, large red decal, 41"w x 22"d x 29"h, excellent condition   5500-7500
March 3, 1996
Sold for $7000

1136. Gustav Stickley screen, #83, tri-fold, wooden frame has original finish, panels covered in Craftsman canvas fabric in rusty brown color, side panels 66"h, middle panel 67.5"h, width of each 21", red decal, excellent condition
2500-3500   March 27, 1988
Sold for $1800

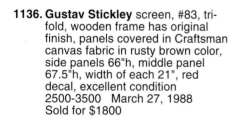

1137. Gustav Stickley dinner gong, tapered posts with applied corbels and arched top rail, series of five supports at base, cleaned original finish, replaced gong and striker, 24"w x 10"d x 37"h, very good condition   5000-7000   November 24, 1996
Sold for $5000

1138. Gustav Stickley wood basket, attribution, similar to #236, hammered curled iron base supporting beveled oak slats and hammered iron tacks, original finish, unsigned, 31"w x 26"d x 12"h, excellent condition   5500-7500 May 19, 1996
Sold for $7000

1139. Gustav Stickley
window seat, #178, vertical thru-tenon arms over original leather seat and tacks, some stains to leather, keyed lower horizontal stretcher, original finish, some wear to bottom of feet, signed with a large red decal, 36"w x 19"d x 26"h, very good condition 1500-2000
May 15, 1994
Sold for $3500

Not Pictured:

1140. Gustav Stickley
window seat, #177, original leather and tacks, inverted V-seat rail above a wide keyed tenon stretcher, original finish, red decal, 25"w x 19"d x 26"h, excellent condition   3000-4000
November 14, 1993
Sold for $3250
Note: Same form as #178 only more narrow.

1141. Gustav Stickley hall seat, thru-tenon construction with a lift seat, recent finish, red decal, 24"w x 18"d x 28"h, very good condition   3500-4500
February 16, 1997   Sold for $3000

1142. Gustav Stickley stand, similar to #642 with backsplash, two small drawers over one large drawer, wooden knobs, recoated, original finish, branded, 22"w x 16"d x 29"h, small burn to top, very good condition 1000-1500   May 2, 1993   Sold for $1600

1143. Gustav Stickley sewing table, #630, three drawers with original wooden knobs and two 12" drop leaves, cleaned finish, signed with red decal and paper label, 17"w x 17"d x 28"h, very good condition 1500-2000   November 24, 1996   Sold for $2000

Not Pictured:

1144. Gustav Stickley sewing table, #630, original finish, signed with red decal, minor repair to one drawer, good condition   800-1200   May 7, 1989 Sold for $1100

1145. Gustav Stickley sewing table, #630, original finish with slight stains to top, paper label and branded, excellent condition   1000-1500 September 30, 1990   Sold for $2000

1146. Gustav Stickley sewing table, #630, recent finish, paper label and red decal, very good condition 1500-2000   February 12, 1995   Sold for $1700

1147. Gustav Stickley mantle clock, thru-tenons at lower bottom and exposed dovetailing at top, brass face with impressed company logo behind door with leaded panel showing a brass pendulum with Seth Thomas movement, original finish, branded signature on back, 8.5"w x 5"d x 14"h, excellent condition   4000-6000   May 21, 1995 Sold for $6000

Not Pictured:

1148. L & JG Stickley music cabinet #70, with amber glass in the door, two adjustable shelves, original finish, 20"w x 16"d x 46.5"h, excellent condition 5000-6000   May 7, 1989   Sold for $5000

1149. Gustav Stickley mantle clock, face with impressed company logo behind door lightly cleaned face, original finish, excellent condition   4000-6000 November 24, 1996   Sold for $8000

1150. L & JG Stickley mantle clock, tapered rectangular case with applied square details sits atop beveled foot, rectangular window shows pendulum, round copper face with original patina, flaring overhang at top, recoated original finish, signed with decal, 16"w x 8"d x 22"h, excellent condition 9000-12,000   December 3, 1995   Sold for $8500

Gustav Stickley
Furniture Marks

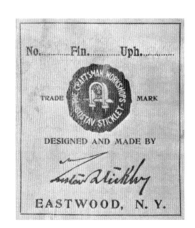

231

Index

To buy, consign or sell these objects call:
(513) 321-6742 or (708) 383-5234

Index

AUCTION & BOOK CREDITS

Owners/Sale Managers-
Don Treadway
Jerri Durham   **John Toomey**
2029 Madison Road   818 North Boulevard
Cincinnati, Ohio 45208   Oak Park, IL 60301
Voice: (513) 321-6742   Voice: (708) 383-5234
Fax: (513) 871-7722   Fax: (708) 383-4828

Auctioneer/owner for Treadway Gallery • **Jerri Nelson Durham**

Auctioneer • **Michael DeFina, Jennifur Condon**

Photographer • **Joseph Higgins**

Computer Treatments • **Stephen Large, Linda Lange** and **Teresa Dorsey**

Treadway Internet: **check our site on the World Wide Web for the latest information: http://www.treadwaygallery.com**

Staff:
Cincinnati • **Thierry Lorthioir, Richard Meyer, Melissa Scheben, Matt Rainey, Teresa Dorsey** and **Stephen Large**

Chicago • **Anne Dickinson, Elizabeth Hobart, Amy Morton** and **Dave Thomas**

Photos: **All Rights Reserved ©1998 Treadway Gallery**

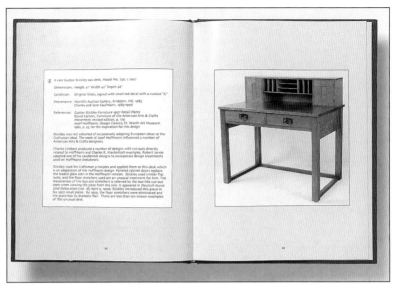

I'd like to offer my gratitude to the craftsmen and artists that designed and produced this furniture. Without their vision and efforts none of this would be possible. My thanks are also extended to the sellers, consignors and buyers of this furniture who's support has helped to produce our 20th Century sales over the past decade.

Don Treadway 1998

To buy, consign or sell these objects call:
(513) 321-6742 or (708) 383-5234

Arts & Crafts Furniture
Reference Book